# Organisms

## TEACHER'S GUIDE

## SCIENCE AND TECHNOLOGY FOR CHILDREN™

**NATIONAL SCIENCE RESOURCES CENTER**
Smithsonian Institution • National Academy of Sciences
Arts and Industries Building, Room 1201
Washington, DC 20560

# NSRC

The National Science Resources Center is operated by the Smithsonian Institution and the National Academy of Sciences to improve the teaching of science in the nation's schools. The NSRC collects and disseminates information about exemplary teaching resources, develops and disseminates curriculum materials, and sponsors outreach activities, specifically in the areas of leadership development and technical assistance, to help school districts develop and sustain hands-on science programs.

## STC Project Supporters

National Science Foundation
Smithsonian Institution
U.S. Department of Defense
U.S. Department of Education
John D. and Catherine T. MacArthur Foundation
The Dow Chemical Company Foundation
E. I. du Pont de Nemours & Company
Amoco Foundation, Inc.
Hewlett-Packard Company
Smithsonian Institution Educational Outreach Fund
Smithsonian Women's Committee

This project was supported, in part,
by the
**National Science Foundation**
Opinions expressed are those of the authors
and not necessarily those of the Foundation

ISBN 0-89278-735-X

Published by Carolina Biological Supply Company, 2700 York Road, Burlington, NC 27215.
Call toll free 1-800-334-5551.

This material is based upon work supported by the National Science Foundation under Grant No. ESI-9252947. Any opinions, findings, and conclusions or recommendations expressed in this material are those of the author(s) and do not necessarily reflect the views of the National Science Foundation.

CB787249812

⊕ Printed on recycled paper.

# Foreword

Since 1988, the National Science Resources Center (NSRC) has been developing Science and Technology for Children (STC), an innovative hands-on science program for children in grades one through six. The 24 units of the STC program, four for each grade level, are designed to provide all students with stimulating experiences in the life, earth, and physical sciences and technology while simultaneously developing their critical-thinking and problem-solving skills.

## Sequence of STC Units

| Grade | Life, Earth, and Physical Sciences and Technology | | | |
|-------|-------|-------|-------|-------|
| 1 | Organisms | Weather | Solids and Liquids | Comparing and Measuring |
| 2 | The Life Cycle of Butterflies | Soils | Changes | Balancing and Weighing |
| 3 | Plant Growth and Development | Rocks and Minerals | Chemical Tests | Sound |
| 4 | Animal Studies | Land and Water | Electric Circuits | Motion and Design |
| 5 | Microworlds | Ecosystems | Food Chemistry | Floating and Sinking |
| 6 | Experiments with Plants | Measuring Time | Magnets and Motors | The Technology of Paper |

The STC units provide children with the opportunity to learn age-appropriate concepts and skills and to acquire scientific attitudes and habits of mind. In the primary grades, children begin their study of science by observing, measuring, and identifying properties. Then they move on through a progression of experiences that culminate in grade six with the design of controlled experiments.

## Sequence of Development of Scientific Reasoning Skills

| Scientific Reasoning Skills | Grades | | | | | |
|-----------------------------|---|---|---|---|---|---|
| | 1 | 2 | 3 | 4 | 5 | 6 |
| Observing, Measuring, and Identifying Properties | ♦ | ♦ | ♦ | ♦ | ♦ | ♦ |
| Seeking Evidence Recognizing Patterns and Cycles | | ♦ | ♦ | ♦ | ♦ | ♦ |
| Identifying Cause and Effect Extending the Senses | | | | ♦ | ♦ | ♦ |
| Designing and Conducting Controlled Experiments | | | | | | ♦ |

The "Focus-Explore-Reflect-Apply" learning cycle incorporated into the STC units is based on research findings about children's learning. These findings indicate that knowledge is actively constructed by each learner and that children learn science best in a hands-on experimental environment where they can make their own discoveries. The steps of the learning cycle are as follows:

- Focus: Explore and clarify the ideas that children already have about the topic.

- Explore: Enable children to engage in hands-on explorations of the objects, organisms, and science phenomena to be investigated.

- Reflect: Encourage children to discuss their observations and to reconcile their ideas.

- Apply: Help children discuss and apply their new ideas in new situations.

The learning cycle in STC units gives students opportunities to develop increased understanding of important scientific concepts and to develop positive attitudes toward science.

The STC units provide teachers with a variety of strategies with which to assess student learning. The STC units also offer teachers opportunities to link the teaching of science with the development of skills in mathematics, language arts, and social studies. In addition, the STC units encourage the use of cooperative learning to help students develop the valuable skill of working together.

In the extensive research and development process used with all STC units, scientists and educators, including experienced elementary school teachers, act as consultants to teacher-developers, who research, trial teach, and write the units. The process begins with the developer researching the unit's content and pedagogy. Then, before writing the unit, the developer trial teaches lessons in public school classrooms in the metropolitan Washington, D.C., area. Once a unit is written, the NSRC evaluates its effectiveness with children by field-testing it nationally in ethnically diverse urban, rural, and suburban public schools. At the field-testing stage, the assessment sections in each unit are also evaluated by the Program Evaluation and Research Group of Lesley College, located in Cambridge, Mass. The final editions of the units reflect the incorporation of teacher and student field-test feedback and of comments on accuracy and soundness from the leading scientists and science educators who serve on the STC Advisory Panel.

The STC project would not have been possible without the generous support of numerous federal agencies, private foundations, and corporations. Supporters include the National Science Foundation, the Smithsonian Institution, the U.S. Department of Defense, the U.S. Department of Education, the John D. and Catherine T. MacArthur Foundation, the Dow Chemical Company Foundation, the Amoco Foundation, Inc., E. I. du Pont de Nemours & Company, the Hewlett-Packard Company, the Smithsonian Institution Educational Outreach Fund, and the Smithsonian Women's Committee.

# Acknowledgments

*O*rganisms was researched and developed by Wendy Binder, edited by Lynn Miller, and illustrated by Max-Karl Winkler. Other NSRC staff who contributed to the development and production of this unit include Sally Goetz Shuler, deputy director for development, external relations, and outreach; Joyce Lowry Weiskopf, STC project director; Dean Trackman, publications director; and Heidi M. Kupke, publications technology specialist. The unit was evaluated by Sabra Price, senior research associate, Program Evaluation and Research Group, Lesley College. *Organisms* was trial taught in Lisa Morse's first-grade classroom at Glebe Elementary School in Arlington, Virginia.

The technical review of *Organisms* was conducted by:

Sally H. Love, Exhibit Developer, Office of Public Programs, National Museum of Natural History, Smithsonian Institution, Washington, DC

Dr. Roland Shelley, Biologist, North Carolina State Museum of Natural Sciences, Raleigh, North Carolina

Dr. Calvin R. Sperling, Plant Exploration Officer, United States Department of Agricultural Research Services, Beltsville, MD

The unit was nationally field-tested in the following school sites with the cooperation of the individuals listed:

*Denver Public Schools, Denver CO*
Coordinator: Judy Curtis, Elementary Science Coordinator
Barbara Culbertson, Teacher, Traylor Academy
Staci Porter, Teacher, Montclair Elementary School
Sandy Stokely, Teacher, Ellis Elementary School

*Lee County School District, Tupelo, MS*
Coordinator: Amelia Anglin, Elementary Curriculum Coordinator
Lillian Botts, Teacher, Shannon Elementary School
Carolyn Crouch, Teacher, Saltillo Elementary School
Cindy Ellis, Teacher, Verona Elementary School

*Cupertino Union School District, Cupertino, CA*
Coordinator: Mary Barbara Zorio, Resource Teacher
Nancy Day, Teacher, Fremont Older School
MaryAnn Hudson, Teacher, Montclaire School
Barbara Peterson, Teacher, Garden Gate School

*Montgomery County School District, Rockville, MD*
Coordinator: Bill MacDonald, Coordinator of Elementary Science
Janice Bauer, Teacher, Twinbrook School
Maggie Brogdon, Teacher, Strawberry Knoll School
Robin Gross, Teacher, Lois P. Rockwell School
Barbara Rubin, Teacher, Rosemont School

The NSRC would also like to thank the following individuals for their contributions to this unit:

Dr. Peter P. Afflerbach, Associate Professor, National Reading Research Center, University of Maryland, College Park, MD

Tim Atkinson, Department Head, Botany, Carolina Biological Supply Company, Burlington, NC

Thomas Bowman, Curator, Department of Invertebrate Zoology, National Museum of American History, Smithsonian Institution, Washington, DC

Catherine Corder, NSRC Publications Technology Specialist (1992–93), Washington, DC

Michael Davenport, Collection Manager, Department of Herpetology, National Zoological Park, Smithsonian Institution, Washington, DC

Debby Deal, Elementary School Curriculum Consultant, Fairfax Station, VA

Robert Herschler, Curator, Department of Invertebrate Zoology, National Museum of American History, Smithsonian Institution, Washington, DC

Gary Hevel, Collections Manager, Department of Entomology, National Museum of American History, Smithsonian Institution, Washington, DC

Kathleen Johnston, NSRC Publications Director (1989–94), Washington, DC

Linda Kostrzewa, Owner, The Children's Bookshop, Clifton, VA

Eric F. Long, Staff Photographer, Office of Printing and Photographic Services, Smithsonian Institution, Washington, DC

Mary Ellen McCaffrey, Photographic Production Control, Office of Printing and Photographic Services, Smithsonian Institution, Washington, DC

Dane Penland, Chief, Imaging and Technology Services,
    Smithsonian Institution, Washington, DC
Lawrence Wallace, Department Head, Living Zoology,
    Carolina Biological Supply Company, Burlington, NC
Joanne Uyeda, Principal, Glebe Elementary School,
    Arlington, VA
The librarians and staff of the Central Reference
    Service, Smithsonian Institution Libraries,
    Washington, DC

                    Douglas Lapp
                    Executive Director
                    National Science Resources Center

# STC Advisory Panel

# Contents

# Goals for *Organisms*

In this unit, students explore the similarities and differences between plants and animals. Through their experiences, students are introduced to the following concepts, skills, and attitudes.

## Concepts

- We use our senses to observe the world around us.

- Organisms have basic needs, such as food, water, air, space, and shelter.

- Each type of organism has specific needs, such as type of food, amount of water, amount of light, amount of space, and type of shelter.

- There is a wide diversity of living things on earth.

- Organisms grow, change, and die over time.

- Some plants grow from seeds. The roots grow first and then the stem.

- Plants have similarities, such as the ability to grow and the need for water, light, space, and air.

- Animals have similarities, such as the ability to move and the need for food, water, space, and shelter.

- Plants and animals have similarities, such as basic needs, ability to grow and change, and death.

- Humans are similar to other organisms. Humans have basic needs and also grow, change, and die.

## Skills

- Observing and describing the characteristics of seeds and plants.

- Planting seeds and observing and recording their growth.

- Observing and describing the characteristics of a variety of plants and animals in woodland and freshwater environments.

- Recording observations in words and drawings.

- Making comparisons among a variety of plants and animals.

- Communicating ideas through writing, drawing, and discussion.

- Reading to enhance understanding of the basic needs of organisms and the diversity of life.

- Applying what students know about plants and animals to what students know about themselves.

- Maintaining plants and animals outside their natural environments.

## Attitudes

- Developing an interest in exploring the characteristics of plants and animals.

- Gaining an awareness of the diversity of life.

- Developing positive attitudes toward different forms of life.

- Developing an awareness that humans are similar to other living things.

- Developing a sensitivity to the needs of living things.

# Unit Overview and Materials List

Many young children, at one time or another, have asked for a jar, run outside, caught an animal to bring home, and sat watching it for hours. Others have helped plant seeds or gardens and become fascinated as they see plants spring into life.

Children have a natural curiosity about both animals and plants. But few have been asked to look at the two together, to think about how plants and animals are alike and different, and to think about themselves as organisms, too.

*Organisms*, a 16-lesson unit designed for first-graders, gives children the opportunity to explore these likenesses and differences and thereby, to become more aware of the diversity of life. As they investigate a variety of organisms, students discover that organisms have certain basic needs, such as food and water. In addition, they learn that organisms have certain specific needs— needs specific to the type of organism—such as type of water, range of temperature, and type of food. In observing and taking care of a number of different plants and animals, students begin to develop positive attitudes and a sensitivity toward living things.

At this age, children are developing their observation skills. Using more than one sense, they are moving from focusing on one characteristic to focusing on several characteristics at a time. They are beginning to use direct comparisons to identify similarities and differences among objects. In addition, first-graders are starting to classify objects and to give reasons for their classifications.

Children are also developing the ability to relate their concrete experiences, not only through drawing and speaking but also through the written word. Increasingly able to focus on people and things outside themselves, they are starting to listen more to what others have to say and to work more effectively in groups.

The first lesson gets students thinking about what living things need to live and be healthy and about the ways all plants and animals are alike and different. A pre-unit assessment lesson, it provides you with a sense of students' present thinking about the unit's central themes.

Lessons 2 and 3 introduce students to the first organism they will study: plants they grow from seeds. Students create an observing table, a tool that helps them sharpen their observation skills. Throughout the unit, children consult and add to this table. This activity encourages them to use more than one sense as they observe their different organisms.

Moving from how a seed grows into a plant to how plants flourish in their natural homes, student groups set up woodland terraria with moss and young conifer trees in Lesson 4 and freshwater aquaria with *Elodea* and *Cabomba* in Lesson 5. Establishing the process they will use throughout the unit, students observe, record, discuss, and compare features of the two woodland plants and then the two freshwater plants.

In Lesson 6, students return to the seeds they have planted, observed, and cared for over a period of time. Here, for the first time, they focus on growth and change in an organism, discuss what plants need to live, and create their own readers that capture their experiences about growing plants from seeds.

To expand the class's understanding of the diversity of life, Lessons 7 through 10 introduce four animals: freshwater snails and guppies for the aquaria, and pill bugs and Bess beetles (or millipedes) for the terraria. By adding these animals to the two environments, students begin to notice not only that plants coexist with animals but also that animals coexist with other animals. This time, students observe, record, discuss, and use Venn diagrams to compare the two woodland animals and then the two freshwater animals. In addition, by observing a pair of guppies (male and female), they discover that similarities and differences exist within the same kind of organism.

Lessons 11 and 12 reinforce the class's emerging awareness that living things grow and change. Students observe, discuss, and write about changes that have occurred in the terraria and aquaria over time.

Lessons 13 through 15 help students move from the specific to the general, forming their own ideas about the ways plants and animals are alike and different. Using Venn diagrams, students first explore how all their plants are alike and different; then, how all their animals are alike and different; and finally, how all eight of these plants and animals are alike and different. To enhance their understanding of these concepts, in Lesson 13, students read about four unusual plants from around the world. And, to reinforce their awareness of organisms' basic and specific needs, the class reads about how a zoo prepares a home for a new organism, a crocodile.

In Lesson 16, students are ready to apply what they have learned about organisms to the one organism in the classroom they have not yet discussed: themselves. How are we like other organisms? How are we different? Through drawings and words, students compare themselves with other living things.

This is an exciting unit for young students. They get to observe, touch, hold, and care for a number of living things that have been chosen especially for their strikingly different characteristics and that exemplify the variety that exists in nature. By bringing a part of the natural world into the classroom, you give children a deeper understanding of the diversity of life. And you help them see that all living things are like one another in many ways but are also unique unto themselves.

## Materials List

Below is a list of the materials needed for the *Organisms* unit. Please note that the metric and English equivalent measurements in this unit are approximate.

| | |
|---|---|
| 1 | *Organisms* Teacher's Guide |
| *30 | optional *Organisms* Student Notebooks (*My Organisms Book*) |
| 30 | hand lenses |
| 60 | Little Marvel peas |
| 60 | red kidney beans |
| 60 | pumpkin seeds |
| 60 | sunflower seeds |
| 30 | resealable plastic bags, 1 liter (1 qt) |
| 33 | plastic cups, 207 ml (7 oz) |
| 31 | plastic teaspoons |
| 8 | red colored dots |
| 8 | blue colored dots |
| 8 | white colored dots |
| 8 | yellow colored dots |
| | Seed starter potting soil, minimum 16 liters (4 gal) |
| 4 | plant misters |
| 1 | class planter tray and plastic lid, 28 × 53 cm (21 × 11 in) |
| 2 | red plastic plates, 26 cm (10 in) |
| 2 | yellow plastic plates, 26 cm (10 in) |
| 2 | blue plastic plates, 26 cm (10 in) |
| 2 | white plastic plates, 26 cm (10 in) |
| 34 | plant stakes |
| 34 | plastic rings |
| 34 | planter labels |
| 4 | china markers |
| 8 | rolls of transparent tape |
| 2 | Post-it™ notepads, 11 × 15 cm (4 × 6 in) |
| 250 | sheets of 67-lb white paper, 22 × 28 cm (8½ × 11 in) |
| 1 | plastic trash bag, 120 liters (30 gal) |
| 8 | plastic flex tanks and lids, 6 liters (1½ gal) |
| | Woodland terrarium soil, 12 liters (12 qt) |
| *4 | moss mats |
| *7 | tree seedlings |
| 5 | bags of aqua gravel, 2 kg (5 lb) |
| 8 | plastic pails and lids, 4 liters (1 gal) |
| 1 | bottle of tap water conditioner, 60 ml (2 oz) |
| *9 | *Elodea* sprigs |
| *7 | *Cabomba* plants |
| 2 | aquarium dip nets (2 in) |

| | |
|---|---|
| 1 | aquarium thermometer |
| 1 | plastic ladle |
| 8 | plastic flex tanks and lids, 4 liters (1 gal) |
| *18 | guppies, 9 male and 9 female |
| *18 | pond snails |
| 1 | flake fish food, 20 g (¾ oz) |
| 30 | plastic cups and lids, 266 ml (9 oz) |
| *16 | pill bugs |
| *8 | Bess beetles or millipedes |
| 1 | bag of 16 wood chunks |
| 1 | box of disposable plastic gloves |
| 7 | Post-it™ notepads, 38 × 50 mm (1½ × 2 in) |
| 1 | pack of white drawing paper, 30 × 40 cm (12 × 18 in) |

| | |
|---|---|
| ** | Newsprint |
| ** | Leaf litter |
| ** | Large markers |
| ** | Crayons |
| ** | Writing paper |
| ** | Paper towels |
| ** | Newspaper |
| ** | Glue (a container for each group of students works best) |
| ** | Assorted construction paper |
| ** | Colander |
| ** | Butcher paper, 150 × 120 cm (60 × 48 in) for the "Ways Animals Move" graph |
| **1 | trash can, large box, or large bucket |
| ** | Large paper clips |
| ** | Mushrooms or lettuce |
| ** | Scissors or paper cutter (for teacher) |
| ** | Bulletin board pushpin |

*Note: The optional Student Notebooks and the living materials are available from Carolina Biological Supply Company (1-800-334-5551). You will need to order the living materials with the prepaid order cards enclosed in the kit box (see pg. 6 for information on ordering).

**Note: These items are not included in the kit. They are commonly available in most schools or can be brought from home.

# Important Information on Live Materials

## Ordering Live Materials

If you are using the *Organisms* kit of materials from Carolina Biological Supply Company, you will need to order live materials separately by completing the enclosed prepaid order cards:

- Pink card: To order the freshwater and woodland plants for Lessons 4 and 5

- Yellow card: To order the snails and guppies for Lessons 7 and 8

- Blue card: To order the pill bugs and Bess beetles or millipedes for Lessons 9 and 10

Before you begin the unit, decide when you need to receive each group of live materials. These dates will depend on your schedule for teaching the lessons. Carolina Biological Supply Company must receive each card at least 20 business days before your requested delivery date. (If you wish, you can send the cards together before you start the unit.) For this unit, you will receive the live materials in three separate shipments.

Each time you send in an order card, remember to do the following:

- Choose your desired date of arrival. It should be a Wednesday or a Thursday, because your live materials will be shipped on a Monday or a Tuesday.

- Indicate the requested date of arrival on the order card.

- Alert your school's front office to the expected arrival date. Arrange for the boxes to be brought to your room immediately upon delivery. Plan to teach the lesson soon afterward.

- Find out whether exterminators are scheduled to visit your school. If so, be sure they do not treat your classroom while you are teaching the unit.

- Open the carton and remove the live materials as soon as they arrive. See Appendix A for guidance on how to maintain live materials.

If you are not using the *Organisms* kit from Carolina Biological Supply Company, be sure to contact your supplier of live organisms to establish a delivery schedule.

## Why Use These Organisms?

The organisms in this unit were thoroughly researched before they were selected. The selection criteria for each organism included the following:

- The organism supports the goals of the unit.

- The organism is easy to use in the classroom.

- The organism is available year-round.

- The organism can be cultured, or raised (often in a laboratory); therefore, the population of the organism in the wild will not be depleted.

- If the organism is not culturable, research has shown that collecting it from its natural environment will not affect its population or the existing food webs.

- The organism is unlikely to harm local ecosystems.

If you decide to substitute other organisms for those used in this unit, please keep these criteria in mind.

## Bess Beetles and Millipedes

Bess beetles and millipedes are difficult to culture in a laboratory; they can only be collected in the wild during certain seasons. In addition, because it is important to maintain nature's ecological balance, they cannot be overcollected. Therefore, the kit supplies fewer Bess beetles and millipedes than pill bugs, snails, and guppies. Depending upon availability, you will receive either eight Bess beetles or eight millipedes.

**Note:** For information on what to do with the organisms when the unit is over, see Appendix A.

# Teaching *Organisms*

The following information on unit structure, teaching strategies, materials, and assessment will help you give students the guidance they need to make the most of their hands-on experiences with this unit.

## Unit Structure

**How Lessons Are Organized in the Teacher's Guide:** Each lesson in the *Organisms* Teacher's Guide provides you with a brief overview, lesson objectives, key background information, materials list, advance preparation instructions, step-by-step procedures, and helpful management tips. Many of the lessons include recommended guidelines for assessment. Lessons also frequently indicate opportunities for curriculum integration. Look for the following icons that highlight extension ideas:

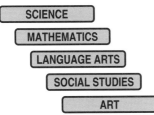

Please note that all record sheets, blackline masters, student instructions, and reading selections may be copied and used in conjunction with the teaching of this unit.

**The *Organisms* Student Notebook:** An optional consumable notebook for students, *My Organisms Book,* has been published for this unit. This notebook includes all record sheets used in the unit. Students will use some of the record sheets to record observations and group work. The notebook also includes a reading selection, "A Crocodile Comes to the Zoo," that students read in Lesson 15.

If you have these notebooks, you may want to consider collecting them periodically to assess student progress. At the conclusion of the unit, students may keep their notebooks as a reminder of all they have learned. If you are not using these notebooks, you will need to copy all record sheets and reading selections for your students.

## Teaching Strategies

**Classroom Discussion:** Class discussions, effectively led by the teacher, are important vehicles for science learning. Research shows that the way questions are asked, as well as the time allowed for responses, can contribute to the quality of the discussion.

When you ask questions, think about what you want to achieve in the ensuing discussion. For example, open-ended questions, for which there is no one right answer, will encourage students to give creative and thoughtful answers. You can use other types of questions to encourage students to see specific relationships and contrasts or to help them summarize and draw conclusions. It is good practice to mix these questions. It also is good practice always to give students "wait time" before expecting them to answer; this will encourage broader participation and more thoughtful answers. You will want to monitor responses, looking for additional situations that invite students to formulate hypotheses, make generalizations, and explain how they arrived at a conclusion.

**Brainstorming:** Brainstorming is a whole-class exercise in which students contribute their thoughts about a particular idea or problem. When used to introduce a new science topic, it can be a stimulating and productive exercise. It also is a useful and efficient way for the teacher to find out what students know and think about a topic. As students learn the rules for brainstorming, they will become increasingly adept in their participation.

To begin a brainstorming session, define for students the topics about which they will share ideas. Explain the following rules to students:

- Accept all ideas without judgment.

- Do not criticize or make unnecessary comments about the contributions of others.

- Try to connect your ideas to the ideas of others.

**Cooperative Learning Groups:** One of the best ways to teach hands-on science is to arrange students in small groups. There are several advantages to this organization. It provides a small forum for students to express their ideas and get feedback. It also offers students a chance to learn from each other by sharing ideas, discoveries, and skills. With coaching, students can develop important interpersonal skills that will serve them well in all aspects of life. As students work, they will often find it productive to talk about what they are doing, resulting in a steady hum of conversation. If you or others in the school are accustomed to a quiet room, this new, busy atmosphere may require some adjustment.

**Venn Diagrams:** The Venn diagram is a useful tool for sorting, classifying, and comparing information. Throughout this unit, you and your students will use Venn diagrams to discover ways in which plants and animals are alike and different.

Venn diagrams use circles to represent different sets of information. For example, the circle in Figure T-1 represents the snail. Words that describe the snail are recorded inside the circle, and words that do not describe the snail are recorded outside the circle.

***Figure T-1:*** *Sample snail Venn diagram*

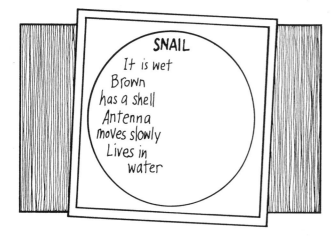

In Figure T-2, Venn diagrams are used to compare two animals. The intersection (or center space) of the circles contains the characteristics that are common to both animals. The rest of each circle contains characteristics unique to the snail or guppy.

***Figure T-2:*** *Sample snail and guppy Venn diagram*

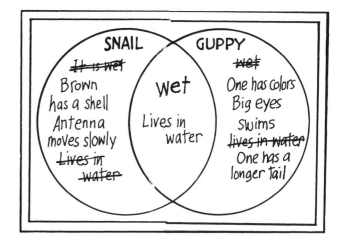

**Learning Centers:** You can give supplemental science materials a permanent home in the classroom in a spot designated as the learning center. Students can use the center in a number of ways: as an "on your own" project center, as an observation post, as a trade-book reading nook, or simply as a place to spend unscheduled time when assignments are done. To keep interest in the center high, change the learning center or add to it often. Here are a few suggestions of items to include:

- Science trade books on plants, animals, habitats, diversity of life (see Bibliography).

- Audiovisual materials on related subjects.

- Items contributed by students for sharing.

## Materials

**Safety Notes:** This unit does not contain anything of a highly toxic nature, but common sense dictates that nothing be put in the mouth. In fact, it is good practice to tell your students that, in science class, materials are never tasted, even food for animals.

**Organization of Materials:** To help ensure an orderly progression through the unit, you will need to establish a system for storing and distributing materials. Being prepared is the key to success.

- Read through the Materials List on pg. 5. Begin to collect the needed items not provided in the kit.

- Preview each lesson to familiarize yourself with the materials needed that day. A few lessons require advance preparation. In those cases, a Management Tip in the preceding lesson will alert you to the need for advance preparation.

- Management tips are provided throughout the unit. Look for the icon at the right.

## Assessment

**Philosophy:** In the Science and Technology for Children program, assessment is an ongoing, integral part of instruction. Because assessment emerges naturally from the activities in the lessons, students are assessed in the same manner in which they are taught. They may, for example, perform experiments, record their observations, or make oral presentations. Such assessments permit the examination of processes as well as of products, emphasizing what students know and can do.

The learning goals in STC units include a number of different science concepts, skills, and attitudes. Therefore, a number of different strategies are provided to help you assess and document your students' progress toward the goals (see Figure T-3). These strategies also will help you report to parents and appraise your own teaching. In addition, the assessments will enable your students to view their own progress, reflect on their learning, and formulate further questions for investigation and research.

Figure T-3 summarizes the goals and assessment strategies for this unit. The left-hand column lists the individual goals for the *Organisms* unit and the lessons in which they are addressed. The right-hand column identifies lessons containing assessment sections to which you can turn for specific assessment strategies. These strategies are summarized as bulleted items.

**Assessment Strategies:** The assessment strategies in STC units fall into three categories: matched pre- and post-unit assessments, embedded assessments, and additional assessments.

The first lesson of each STC unit is a *pre-unit assessment* designed to give you information about what the whole class and individual students already know about the unit's topic and what they want to find out. It often includes a brainstorming session during which students share their thoughts about the topic through exploring one or two basic questions. In the *post-unit assessment* following the final lesson, the class revisits the pre-unit assessment questions, giving you two sets of comparable data that indicate students' growth in knowledge and skills.

Throughout a unit, assessments are incorporated, or embedded, into lessons. These *embedded assessments* are activities that occur naturally within the context of both the individual lesson and the unit as a whole; they are often indistinguishable from instructional activities. By providing structured activities and guidelines for assessing students' progress and thinking, embedded assessments contribute to an ongoing, detailed profile of growth. In many STC units, the last lesson is an embedded assessment that challenges students to synthesize and apply concepts or skills from the unit.

*Additional assessments* can be used to determine students' understanding after the unit has been completed. In these assessments, students may work with materials to solve problems, conduct experiments, or interpret and organize data. In grades three through six, they may also complete self-assessments or paper-and-pencil tests. When you are selecting additional assessments, consider using more than one assessment to give students with different learning styles opportunities to express their knowledge and skills.

**Documenting Student Performance:** In STC units, assessment is based on your recorded observations, students' work products, and oral communication. All these documentation methods combine to give you a comprehensive picture of each student's growth.

Teachers' *observations and anecdotal notes* often provide the most useful information about students' understanding, especially in the early grades when some students are not yet writing their ideas fluently. Because it is important to document observations used for assessment, teachers frequently keep note cards, journals, or checklists. Many lessons include guidelines to help you focus your observations. The blackline master on pg. 14 provides a format you may want to use or adapt for recording observations. It includes this unit's goals for science concepts and skills.

*Work products,* which include both what students write and what they make, indicate students' progress toward the goals of the unit. Children produce a variety of written materials during a unit. Record sheets, which include written observations, drawings, graphs, tables, and charts, are an important part of all STC units. They provide evidence of each student's ability to collect, record, and process information. Students' science journals are another type of work product. In grades one and two, journal

*continued on pg. 13*

## *Organisms*: Goals and Assessment Strategies

| Concepts | |
|---|---|
| **Goals** | **Assessment Strategies** |
| We use our senses to observe the world around us.<br>  Lessons 2–16 | Lessons 2, 4, 6, 9–10<br> ▪ Record sheets<br> ▪ Class discussions<br> ▪ Planting cards<br> ▪ Class language experience story<br> ▪ Teacher's observations |
| Organisms have basic needs, such as food, water, air, space, and shelter.<br>  Lessons 1–16 | Lessons 1, 6, 8, 10, 15–16, and Additional Assessments 1–3<br> ▪ Pre- and post-unit assessments<br> ▪ Record sheets<br> ▪ Class lists and discussions<br> ▪ Class language experience story<br> ▪ Blackline masters<br> ▪ Venn diagrams |
| Each type of organism has specific needs, such as type of food, amount of water, amount of light, amount of space, and type of shelter.<br>  Lessons 1–16 | Lessons 1, 6, 8, 10, 15–16<br> ▪ Pre- and post-unit assessments<br> ▪ Record sheets<br> ▪ Class lists and discussions<br> ▪ Class language experience story<br> ▪ Venn diagrams |
| There is a wide diversity of living things on earth.<br>  Lessons 1–16 | Lessons 1, 8, 15<br> ▪ Pre- and post-unit assessments<br> ▪ Record sheets<br> ▪ Class lists and discussions |
| Organisms grow, change, and die over time.<br>  Lessons 1, 3–16 | Lessons 1, 6, 11, 16<br> ▪ Record sheets<br> ▪ Class discussions<br> ▪ Planting cards<br> ▪ Class language experience story<br> ▪ Venn diagrams |
| Some plants grow from seeds. The roots grow first and then the stem.<br>  Lessons 2–6 | Lessons 2, 6<br> ▪ Class lists and discussions<br> ▪ Planting cards<br> ▪ Class language experience story |
| Plants have similarities, such as the ability to grow and the need for water, light, space, and air.<br>  Lessons 1–16 | Lessons 1, 6, 15, and Additional Assessments 1, 3<br> ▪ Record sheets<br> ▪ Class lists and discussions<br> ▪ Class language experience story<br> ▪ Venn diagrams |
| Animals have similarities, such as the ability to move and the need for food, water, space, and shelter.<br>  Lessons 1, 6–16 | Lessons 1, 8, 10, 15, and Additional Assessments 1, 3<br> ▪ Record sheets<br> ▪ Class lists and discussions<br> ▪ Venn diagrams |
| Plants and animals have similarities, such as basic needs, ability to grow and change, and death.<br>  Lessons 1, 4–5, 11–16 | Lessons 1, 15–16, and Additional Assessments 1, 3<br> ▪ Pre- and post-unit assessments<br> ▪ Record sheets<br> ▪ Class lists and discussions<br> ▪ Venn diagrams |
| Humans are similar to other organisms. Humans have basic needs and also grow, change, and die.<br>  Lesson 16 | Lesson 16<br> ▪ Pre- and post-unit assessments<br> ▪ Class discussions<br> ▪ Venn diagrams<br> ▪ Student writing |

| Skills | |
|---|---|
| **Goals** | **Assessment Strategies** |
| Observing and describing the characteristics of seeds and the plants that grow from them.<br>  Lessons 2–6 | Lessons 2, 4, 6<br>  ▪ Record sheets<br>  ▪ Class lists and discussions<br>  ▪ Class language experience story |
| Planting seeds and observing and recording their growth.<br>  Lessons 3–6 | Lesson 6<br>  ▪ Planting cards<br>  ▪ Class lists and discussions<br>  ▪ Class language experience story<br>  ▪ Teacher's observations |
| Observing and describing the characteristics of a variety of plants and animals in woodland and freshwater environments.<br>  Lessons 4–16 | Lessons 4, 7–8, 10–11, 15, and Additional Assessments 1, 3<br>  ▪ Record sheets<br>  ▪ Class lists and discussions<br>  ▪ Blackline masters<br>  ▪ Journal sheets<br>  ▪ Venn diagrams |
| Recording observations in words and drawings.<br>  Lessons 2–16 | Lessons 2, 4, 6–11<br>  ▪ Record sheets<br>  ▪ Class lists and discussions<br>  ▪ Blackline masters<br>  ▪ Journal sheets<br>  ▪ Venn diagrams<br>  ▪ Student writing |
| Making comparisons among a variety of plants and animals.<br>  Lessons 4–6, 8, 10, 11–16 | Lessons 4, 6, 8, 10, 15–16, and Additional Assessments 1–3<br>  ▪ Class lists and discussions<br>  ▪ Venn diagrams |
| Communicating ideas through writing, drawing, and discussion.<br>  Lessons 1–16 | Lessons 1–2, 4, 6–11, 15, and Additional Assessments 1–3<br>  ▪ Pre- and post-unit assessments<br>  ▪ Record sheets<br>  ▪ Class lists and discussions<br>  ▪ Planting cards<br>  ▪ Journal sheets<br>  ▪ Class language experience story<br>  ▪ Student writing<br>  ▪ Teacher's observations |
| Reading to enhance understanding of the basic needs of organisms and the diversity of life.<br>  Lessons 13, 15 | Lesson 15<br>  ▪ Class discussions<br>  ▪ Blackline masters<br>  ▪ Teacher's observations |
| Applying what students have learned about plants and animals to what students know about themselves.<br>  Lesson 1, 16 | Lesson 16 and Additional Assessments 1–3<br>  ▪ Pre- and post-unit assessments<br>  ▪ Venn diagrams<br>  ▪ Class discussions<br>  ▪ Student writing |
| Maintaining plants and animals outside their natural environments.<br>  Lessons 3–16 | Lessons 6, 8, and Additional Assessments 1, 3<br>  ▪ Teacher's observations<br>  ▪ Class discussions |

| Attitudes | |
|---|---|
| **Goals** | **Assessment Strategies** |
| Developing an interest in exploring the characteristics of plants and animals.<br>    Lessons 2–16 | Lessons 4, 6, 8, 10–11, 16, and Additional Assessments 1, 3<br>  ■ Class discussions<br>  ■ Teacher's observations |
| Gaining an awareness of the diversity of life.<br>    Lessons 1–16 | Lessons 1, 8, 15<br>  ■ Pre- and post-unit assessments<br>  ■ Class lists and discussions<br>  ■ Teacher's observations<br>  ■ Record sheets |
| Developing positive attitudes toward different forms of life.<br>    Lessons 3–16 | Lessons 7–8, 10<br>  ■ Teacher's observations<br>  ■ Class discussions |
| Developing an awareness that humans are similar to other living things.<br>    Lesson 16 | Lesson 16 and Additional Assessments 1, 3<br>  ■ Pre- and post-unit assessments<br>  ■ Class discussions<br>  ■ Venn diagrams<br>  ■ Teacher's observations<br>  ■ Student writing |
| Developing a sensitivity to the needs of living things.<br>    Lessons 3–16 | Lessons 6, 8, 10, 16, and Additional Assessments 1, 3<br>  ■ Class discussions<br>  ■ Teacher's observations |

*continued from pg. 9*

writings are primarily suggested as extension activities in many lessons. Often a rich source of information for assessment, these journal writings reveal students' thoughts, ideas, and questions over time.

Students' written work products should be kept together in folders to document learning over the course of the unit. When students refer back to their work from previous lessons, they can reflect on their learning. In some cases, students do not write or draw well enough for their products to be used for assessment purposes, but their experiences do contribute to the development of scientific literacy.

*Oral communication*—what students say formally and informally in class and in individual sessions with you—is a particularly useful way to learn what students know. This unit provides your students with many opportunities to share and discuss their own ideas, observations, and opinions. Some young children may be experiencing such activities for the first time. Encourage students to participate in discussions, and stress that there are no right or wrong responses. Creating an environment in which students feel secure expressing their own ideas can stimulate rich and diverse discussions.

Individual and group presentations can give you insights about the meanings your students have assigned to procedures and concepts and about their confidence in their learning. In fact, a student's verbal description of a chart, experiment, or graph is frequently more useful for assessment than the product or results. Questions posed by other students following presentations provide yet another opportunity for you to gather information. Ongoing records of discussions and presentations should be a part of your documentation of students' learning.

## *Organisms:* Observations of Student Performance

| STUDENT'S NAME: | |
|---|---|
| **Concepts** | **Observations** |

**Concepts**

- We use our senses to observe the world around us.

- Organisms have basic needs, such as food, water, air, space, and shelter.

- Each type of organism has specific needs, such as type of food, amount of water, amount of light, amount of space, and type of shelter.

- There is a wide diversity of living things on earth.

- Organisms grow, change, and die over time.

- Some plants grow from seeds. The roots grow first and then the stem.

- Plants have similarities, such as the ability to grow and the need for water, light, space, and air.

- Animals have similarities, such as the ability to move and the need for food, water, space, and shelter.

- Plants and animals have similarities, such as their basic needs, ability to grow and change, and death.

- Humans are similar to other organisms. Humans have basic needs and also grow, change, and die.

**Skills**

- Observing and describing the characteristics of seeds and plants.

- Planting seeds and observing and recording their growth.

- Observing and describing the characteristics of a variety of plants and animals in woodland and freshwater environments.

- Recording observations in words and drawings.

- Making comparisons among a variety of plants and animals.

- Communicating ideas through writing, drawing, and discussion.

- Reading to enhance understanding of the basic needs of organisms and the diversity of life.

- Applying what students have learned about plants and animals to what students know about themselves.

- Maintaining plants and animals outside their natural environments.

# Sharing What We Know about Organisms

**Overview and Objectives**

What are some living things, or "organisms"? How are organisms alike? How are they different? What do they need to live and be healthy?

This lesson involves students in thinking and talking about these questions, and enables you to assess their existing knowledge about plants and animals. Lesson activities generate important pre-unit assessment products. These products can help you evaluate your students' current understanding before the organisms they will study are brought into the classroom.

■ Students draw a living thing and add the elements they think it needs to live and be healthy.

■ Students share the ways they think all plants and animals are alike.

■ Students share the ways they think all plants and animals are different.

**Background**

What do dogs, trees, worms, fungi, and bacteria have in common?

Each is an organism—a living thing. And most living things share the following characteristics:

■ Organisms use energy.

■ Organisms maintain themselves by using food, and they produce waste.

■ Organisms generally are made of one or more cells.

■ Organisms reproduce.

■ Organisms grow, change, or develop.

■ Organisms interact with their surroundings.

■ Organisms have a life span (a beginning and an end).

Though bacteria and fungi are also organisms, this unit focuses on the two kinds of organisms that children of this age are naturally interested in: plants and animals. Many students, for example, will have a family pet or houseplants or gardens at home. The brainstorming session in this lesson will help you find out your students' current thinking about plants and animals. (See pg. 7 of Teaching *Organisms* for more information on brainstorming.)

In this lesson, students individually draw and write about living things. First-graders' writing skill will vary, depending on the point in the school year at which you teach the unit as well as differences in individual ability. To better understand each student's thinking as the lessons progress, you may want to meet with students individually throughout the school day and have them describe their drawings to you. You may also enlist the aid of another adult to help with any dictation students need to do during the lesson itself. Both methods will help you assess students' grasp of key concepts when they are asked to write throughout the unit.

Students will also generate lists describing the ways they think all plants and animals are alike and the ways they are different. While most first-graders can handle the "alike" concept, some may not have any idea how plants and animals are different. It is a good idea to allow a few minutes for the class to share ideas and then let the discussion end naturally. Students will develop more ideas on these concepts as they undergo firsthand experience with organisms, and will revisit these lists later in the unit.

**Note:** You will notice **Record Sheet 1-A: My Living Thing** on the following materials list. If your class is using the Student Notebooks, you will find that they contain all the record sheets students will use throughout the unit. If your class is not using the Student Notebooks, you will need to copy this and all other record sheets for each student whenever a new one is listed in the **Materials** list. Record sheets are found at the ends of the lessons.

## Materials

*For each student*

1   **Record Sheet 1-A: My Living Thing**
1   pencil
1   looseleaf notebook or folder with pockets (for record sheets)

*For the group*

Assorted crayons and markers

*For the class*

3   sheets of newsprint
3   different colored markers
Library books containing pictures of a variety of plants and animals (optional)

## Preparation

1.  Title and date three sheets of newsprint, respectively:

    ■  Our List of Living Things

    ■  Ways We Think Plants and Animals Are Alike

    ■  Ways We Think Plants and Animals Are Different

    Choose a place in the classroom where you can display the lists throughout the unit.

2.  If you plan to use pictures to help launch the brainstorming session (see **Procedure,** Step 5), collect some books illustrating a variety of plants and animals.

3.  Make a copy of **Record Sheet 1-A: My Living Thing** for each student.

**Procedure**

1.  Introduce the unit. Explain that over the next few weeks, the class will be observing and talking about living things, also called organisms.

    **Note:** The terms "organisms" and "living things" are used interchangeably in this unit.

2.  Distribute a copy of **Record Sheet 1-A: My Living Thing** to each student and review it with the class. Ask students to do the following:

    ■ Put your name and today's date on the paper.

    ■ Draw a living thing in the middle of the paper.

    ■ Add to the drawing what you think the living thing needs to live and be healthy.

    ■ Label the parts of the drawing.

    ■ Complete the sentences at the bottom of the drawing (see Figure 1-1).

*Figure 1-1*

*Sample student drawings*

3. Collect the students' drawings and save them for the post-unit assessment activity.

4. Display the large sheet labeled "Our List of Living Things." Ask the class to think of some living things and record their responses. As you record, place a check next to repeat responses to acknowledge all students' contributions.

**Management Tip:** If you would like to do this lesson in two parts, this is a good stopping point.

5. If you are using books to help students brainstorm, show the class some of the plant and animal pictures you have collected. Then show students the sheet labeled "Ways We Think Plants and Animals Are Alike." Ask questions such as the following:

- In what ways are all plants and animals like each other?

- How are all plants and animals the same?

- What are some things you think are true about all plants and animals?

Once again record your students' ideas. Encourage students to listen to each other, both to learn new information and to find out if others share the same ideas. Explain that all ideas will be accepted; ideas are not "right" or "wrong." Sample lists of responses to this question and the next one appear in Figure 1-2.

## Final Activities

1. Now display the sheet labeled "Ways We Think Animals and Plants Are Different." This time, ask the class questions such as the following:

- In what ways are all plants and animals different from each other?

- In what ways are all animals different from plants? Plants different from animals?

As mentioned in the **Background,** allow a few minutes for the students to respond. If the students have no ideas at this point, move on to Step 2.

2. Explain that the lists will stay up during the unit. Students will have a chance to add new ideas to the lists and discuss old ones.

## Extensions

SCIENCE

1. Ask the class to name all of the living things in the classroom. Record students' suggestions on a sheet and revisit this list as the unit progresses.

MATHEMATICS   SCIENCE

2. Have students make individual lists of the living things in their homes or living things they see on the way to school. Keep a class tally of the types and numbers of living things students notice.

**Figure 1-2**

*Sample class lists*

The Ways Plants and
Animals Are Alike

They Grow ✓    They Die
They Live     Some jump
They breathe  They eat food ✓✓
They have grandpas
Some are in deep water

The Ways Plants and
Animals are Different
Animals go all over.
Can live in zoos.
Plants have vines.
Plants need dirt—water.
Plants have stems.
Animals hear.
Animals have moms.
Animals can swim.
Some animals run—fly.
Animals can fight.

## Assessment

This lesson has many assessment opportunities that you can use as a baseline to measure students' progress. You may want to use one or several of them. Record informal observations on charts, cards, or notes to help you keep track of information about each student. The following guidelines are suggested as ways to help you assess your students.

**Record Sheet 1-A: My Living Thing**

- Has each student drawn a living thing? (Most students probably will draw animals.) Was the student able to add one or two things it needs to live? For example: food, water, air, a home (shelter).

- Did the student add other elements to the drawing? For example: other plants or animals.

■ Did the student show relationships between the organism and its environment? For example: a horse eating grass.

**Class List of Living Things**

■ Does the class list of living things include both animals and plants?

■ Does it include any other types of organisms?

■ Does it include any nonliving things?

Bear in mind that most children this age will list animals and possibly one or two plants, such as "flower" or "tree." Animals are more familiar and interesting to many young children than plants; therefore, most of their existing knowledge will be about animals.

**Class Discussion**

■ Can students articulate their thoughts about living things?

■ What information do students already have about plants and animals?

■ In what ways do they think the two are similar? Different?

Most students' statements at this point may focus on specific animals and plants. For example, "A butterfly uses wings." As the unit progresses, students increasingly may be able to make more general statements about plants and animals. For example, "Animals can move."

Throughout the unit, students will be learning important skills basic to science: observing, recording, classifying, and comparing information. You can assess student progress in these skills in two ways: by observing and talking to students as they work individually and in groups; and by looking at individual student products. Both approaches are important.

In the section Teaching *Organisms,* on pgs. 7–15, you will find a detailed discussion about the assessment of students' learning. The specific goals and related assessments for this unit are summarized in Figure T-3 on pgs. 10–12. Please keep in mind that some first-graders may not completely understand every concept and goal listed. As you observe your class, look for the development of these ideas and skills rather than their mastery.

**Note:** At this time, refer to pg. 6 for essential information on ordering your live materials. You will need to send the pink card to order plants for Lessons 4 and 5, the yellow card to order snails and guppies for Lessons 7 and 8, and the blue card to order pill bugs and Bess beetles or millipedes for Lessons 9 and 10.

Take some time now to look at your calendar and decide when to send in the cards. Remember, you need to allow at least 20 business days from the date of order to the date of arrival.

If you are not using the *Organisms* kit from Carolina Biological Supply Company, be sure to contact your supplier of living organisms to establish a delivery schedule.

**Record Sheet 1–A**

Name _____

Date _____

**My Living Thing**

I drew a _____

I think it needs _____

# Observing and Describing Seeds

## Overview and Objectives

In Lesson 1, students began thinking about living things and about how plants and animals are alike and different. Throughout the unit, students will use observation and comparison skills to discover more about these similarities and differences for themselves. By giving students the opportunity to use their senses to take in information about the seeds they will plant in Lesson 3, this lesson helps students begin to develop their observation skills.

- The class discusses ways to find out how the seeds are alike and how they are different.

- Students use their senses to observe a variety of seeds.

- Students draw and describe the seeds.

- Students create a class "observing table" they will use throughout the unit.

## Background

Plants and other producers are essential to life on earth. Without them, many other organisms would soon disappear. We humans, for example, need the oxygen that plants make during photosynthesis, using energy from sunlight. And, numerous life forms depend—directly or indirectly—on plants for food or use them as a source of shelter. There are over 350,000 known types of plants, and many more that scientists have yet to identify.

In this lesson, students begin to explore the variety in plants by observing, describing, and discussing four seeds: kidney bean, pea, sunflower, and pumpkin. All these seeds are edible, which helps emphasize how beneficial plants are to other living things. Most students at this grade level should be able to list more than one property of each seed. Typically, first-graders will discuss the properties one at a time.

**Note:** Beginning with this lesson, students will be asked to record their ideas individually before sharing them with the class. If individual students find the writing too difficult, consider skipping this step and doing only a class write-up of observations.

**Materials**

*For each student*

1   copy of **Observing and Describing Seeds** (blackline master on pg. 32)
1   pencil
1   hand lens
4   seeds (kidney bean, pea, sunflower, pumpkin)
1   plastic bag, 1 liter (1 qt)

*For every two students*

1   bottle of glue

*For the class*

1   copy of **Senses** (blackline master on pg. 33)
2   sheets of newsprint
1   marker
1   roll of transparent tape

**Preparation**

1.   Put a kidney bean, pea, pumpkin seed, and sunflower seed in a plastic bag for each student. You may want to ask students to help you with this.

2.   Prepare the "observing table." Cut out the symbols for the four senses from the blackline master **Senses** (pg. 33). Attach them to a sheet of newsprint (See Figure 2-1).

*Figure 2-1*

*Observing table*

3. Label a sheet of newsprint "What We Think a Seed Is."

4. Copy the blackline master **Observing and Describing Seeds** (pg. 32) for each student.

**Note:** Leave the observing table up to help guide students' observations in later lessons. Students will generate many lists in this unit, all of which capture new discoveries in their own words and therefore document students' learning processes. To help you keep track, write the lesson number and date on each list and whenever possible, leave these lists up in the classroom. If space is limited, consider rotating the lists as they accumulate during the unit. You may also want to string a clothesline in the classroom and hang the lists on it.

**Procedure**

1. Display the sheet labeled "What We Think a Seed Is." Then hold up one of the larger seeds and ask students, "What do you think a seed is?" Record their ideas.

2. Show students one of the plastic bags of seeds. On the chalkboard write the title "How We Could Find Out about Our Seeds." Ask questions such as the following:

   ■ How can we find out about these seeds?

   ■ What could we do to learn about them?

   Record ideas on the chalkboard.

3. Next display the observing table. If students did not suggest looking closely at the seeds, propose that they use their senses to observe the seeds. Help students identify the five senses. Use the table to explain that they will be using four senses—seeing, hearing, smelling, and touching—to observe the seeds. Also let students know that the sense of taste is not used in science class.

**Management Tip:** If your students have not used hand lenses before, take a little time to explore their use. An effective way to use the hand lens is to hold the object stationary and to move the hand lens back and forth above it until the object comes into focus. You may also want to set up a learning center on lenses. Provide a variety of objects, such as feathers, rocks, or other seeds, for the students to observe.

4. Give each student a bag of seeds, a hand lens, and a copy of **Observing and Describing Seeds.** Hand out a bottle of glue to every two students.

   **Note:** Some of your students will probably recognize some of the seeds; however, do not tell the students the seeds' names at this time. An activity in Lesson 6 will enable students to discover the seed types on their own.

5. Now go over Observing and Describing Seeds with the class. Explain that you would like students to use their four senses to find out as much as they can about the seeds. Ask them to write on this sheet what they learn about each seed. Explain that you will observe the first seed together.

**Management Tip:** Depending on the level of students' observing and describing skills, you may want to have them work individually or in pairs for this activity.

6. Using the green seed, ask such questions as the following:

   ■ What can we learn about this seed by using our sense of sight?

   ■ What do your eyes tell you about this seed? (Past student responses have included, "It's green" and "It's round.")

List the responses on the chalkboard.

Have students record class observations on their Observing and Describing Seeds sheet in the box under the eye symbol. If the list is long, help students decide what to record.

7. Using this list, ask students to suggest questions that can be answered through the sense of sight, such as "What color is it?" Record these questions on the observing table. Use Figure 2-2 as a model.

**Figure 2-2**

*Observing table with sample questions*

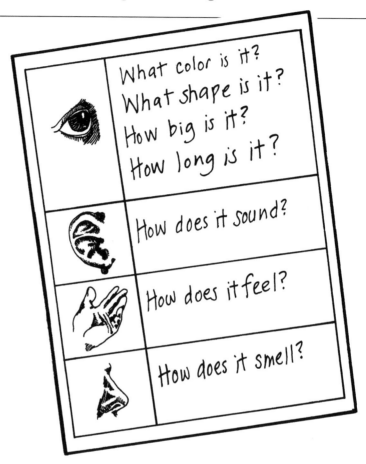

8. To complete the chart for the green seed, repeat Steps 6 and 7 for the other three senses.

   **Note:** Demonstrate how to use the sense of smell in science class (see Figure 2-3).

9. Have students glue the green seed in the first seed box on their Observing and Describing Seeds sheets. You may also want to put tape over the seeds to hold them in place.

10. Read aloud those questions on the observing table that our senses can answer. Encourage students to use these questions as a guide as they observe the other three seeds. Explain that they can record a word or two instead of a whole sentence to describe each seed. Have students complete the sheet for the remaining seeds.

**Figure 2-3**

*Using your sense of smell*

**Final Activities**

1. Using the **Observing and Describing Seeds** sheet, ask students questions similar to the following:

   ■ How are all the seeds alike?

   ■ How are all the seeds different?

2. Revisit the "How We Could Find Out about Our Seeds" list. Now that students have observed the seeds carefully, ask what else they might do to learn more about the seeds. Add any new ideas to the list.

3. If "planting the seed" is not on the class list, explain that in the next lesson students will learn more about the seeds by planting them. Invite students to bring in a seed from home to plant, as well.

4. Collect the seeds and hand lenses. Save the plastic bags to use in Lesson 3.

5. Have students put their Observing and Describing Seeds sheet in their folders.

**Extensions**

| SCIENCE | LANGUAGE ARTS |

1. With the class, read books that help students become better observers, such as *Look! Look! Look!* by Tana Hoban (see Bibliography).

| MATHEMATICS | SCIENCE |

2. Have students bring in packages of seeds from home and then sort them by color, size, shape, or feel. Make a class graph based on one or more of these characteristics.

| LANGUAGE ARTS |

3. To give students more practice in describing, put objects in "feely bags." Ask students to use their sense of touch to discover what the object in the bag is. Then have students describe the object.

| ART | | SCIENCE |

4. Take the class outdoors and have students use their senses of sight and touch to do natural texture rubbings on newsprint. Have them create a collage of the rubbings.

| ART | | SCIENCE |

5. Have students create a drawing that accompanies the title "This is a picture of something I like to (see, hear, touch, or smell)."

## Assessment

Two skills integral to this unit are observing and recording. In this lesson, students record observations for the first time, using the **Observing and Describing Seeds** sheet. Use the following criteria to help you assess students' observational skills at this early stage:

- Are students making observations using one, two, three, or four senses? Bear in mind that students of this age will vary in their ability to name more than one characteristic of an object when observing. For example, they are more likely to say, "It is round" than "It is round, green, and hard."

- Do the descriptions match the object? Is what they have written observable rather than based on past experience? For example: "It is green" versus "I can eat this seed."

Save the Observing and Describing Seeds sheets to compare with other student work at the end of the unit. In addition, think about the following items:

- What do students think a seed is?

- Are students aware that some plants grow from seeds?

While recorded information is useful, also remember that much of what we learn and can assess about the growth of students of this age comes from observing and talking to them. Therefore, you may want to keep anecdotal notes on each student and focus on specific individuals or teams in each lesson. Possible observations include:

- Records observations in words and pictures

- Talks about what is being observed

- Uses adjectives when verbalizing observations

- Exhibits sensitivity toward organisms

- Follows directions and routines

- Takes initiative in his or her work

- Works well with and respects others

- Shares ideas with others in both small and large groups

- Shows interest and curiosity

**Note:** You may want to provide each student with a pocketed folder to hold his or her work products.

**Management Tips:** In Lesson 3, students will plant their seeds. Try to do this on a Monday or Tuesday to give students the greatest chance to observe the very beginning of germination.

Before you teach Lesson 3, you need to moisten the potting soil. Find a large bucket, or line a cardboard box or class trash pail with a plastic trash bag. Place the soil in the container and mix in warm water a cup at a time until the soil is thoroughly moist but not wet.

The preparation time for Lesson 3 is long. Read ahead now to see when you will need to begin. You may also want to enlist the aid of an adult volunteer to assist with the planting in Lesson 3.

**Observing and
Describing Seeds**

Name _____

Date _____

| Seed | 👁 | ✋ | 👃👅 |
|------|---|---|---|
| ⬤ | | | |
| 🫘 | | | |
| ◗ | | | |
| 🌰 | | | |

# Senses

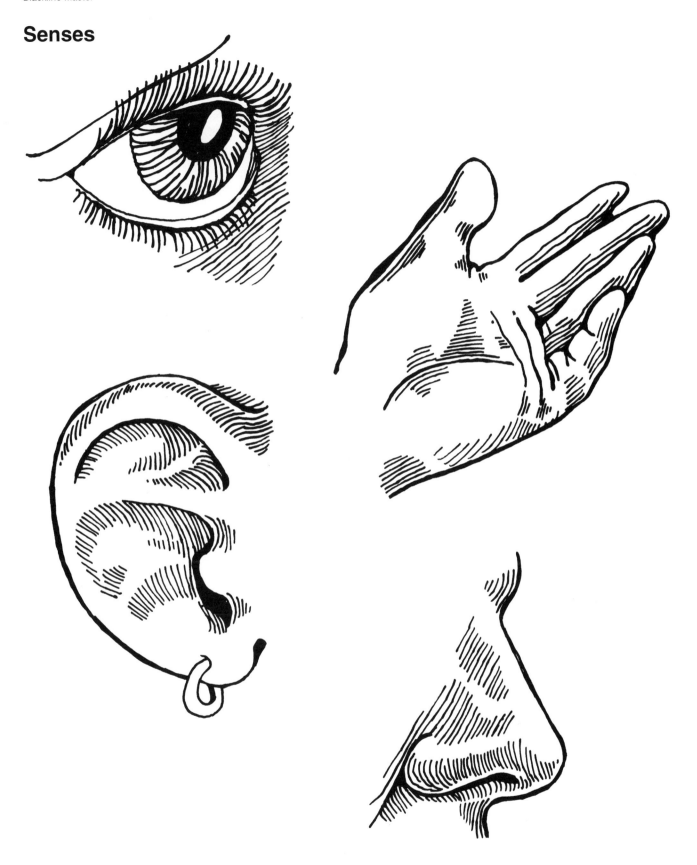

# Planting Our Seeds

**Overview and Objectives**

In this lesson, students plant the seeds they observed in Lesson 2. By planting the seeds and recording the changes, students can naturally connect the relationship of seeds to plants. Growing plants also gives students the opportunity to observe growth and change and the experience of caring for a living thing. In addition, students begin their "planting cards," the tools they will use to record the seeds' growth and development over the next several weeks. By recording their observations in both drawings and words, students are encouraged to make more descriptive observations.

- To begin their exploration of the needs of living things, students plant their seeds.

- Students predict what they think will happen to their seeds.

- Students begin to record their seeds' growth and changes in drawings and words.

**Background**

A seed is a small "life-support" package. Inside each seed is a tiny plant ready to grow. A seed consists of an embryo, from which the seedling develops, a protective seed coat, and a supply of food (oil, carbohydrates, and protein). This food keeps the young plant alive and provides energy for it to start to grow.

In addition to food, almost all plants have similar basic needs to live and be healthy: air, light, water, and a space in which to live. Over the next several lessons, students will discover some of these basic needs.

Germination is the process by which a seed changes to a seedling. Germination starts when the dry, dormant seed is in a damp, warm place. The seed absorbs water and the seed coat breaks open. First, the beginning of the root system appears, growing downward. Then a shoot grows upward and produces the stem and leaves. This young plant is called a seedling (see Figure 3-1).

**Note: Photosynthesis,** the process by which plants use light, water, and carbon dioxide from the air to make their own food, may be too advanced for many children of this age. At this time it is enough for children to know that plants need light, water, air, and a place to live.

**Figure 3-1**

*How a kidney bean grows*

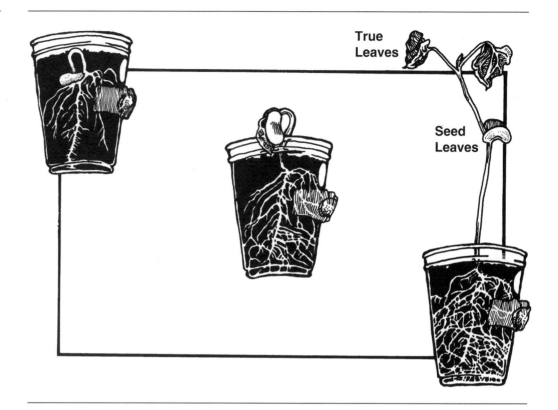

True Leaves

Seed Leaves

**Management Tips:** After this lesson, have students observe their seeds daily and record changes on the planting cards. Students should continue this process until the first true leaves appear (see Figure 3-1) on any of the plants. At that time, you need to skip ahead and teach Lesson 6, and then return to Lessons 4 and 5.

To incorporate this observation activity into their schedules, some teachers have established a "planting center" and made it part of students' morning jobs to check their seeds. To streamline this activity, teachers have also stocked the center with copies of **Planting Card 2** (see pgs. 47–48) and water misters. In addition, teachers have found it useful to have regular "share" times in which students share daily observations and experiences.

**Figure 3-2**

## Planting Table

| Seed | Days to Germination | Planting Depth |
|---|---|---|
| Kidney Bean | 4–8 | 2.5 cm (about 1 in) |
| Pea | 5–10 | 2.5 cm (about 1 in) |
| Sunflower | 5–10 | 1.3 cm (about ½ in) |
| Pumpkin | 5–10 | 2.5 cm (about 1 in) |

# Growing Guidelines

**Water:** A plant needs water to carry nutrients from the soil into the roots and up through the plant, as well as for photosynthesis. Water also keeps the plant erect. Nonetheless, it is important not to over- or underwater your plants. It is best to water them when they need it, rather than on a set schedule.

To tell when the plants need water, students can stick their fingers gently into the soil in the center of their planter cups. If the soil sticks to their fingers or feels moist, the plant does not need water.

It is important to keep the soil moist but not wet. Your students will use plant misters so the seeds will not be washed away and the young seedlings will remain unharmed. Once the plant's root system is well established and visible, students can water the plant with a regular watering can or cup. At that time, they should add water just until it runs out of the drainage hole(s) on the bottom of the planter cup.

**Light and Temperature:** Plants should be placed on a shelf or table near a window. While light is not necessary for seed germination, warmth often is. Most seeds will germinate at room temperature—24°C to 26°C (68°F to 72°F). If you are comfortable, the seeds probably are, too. If your room is cold, place the plantings in the warmer part of the room, but not in the air flow of a heater or air conditioner.

Have the students use the plastic bags provided to cover the plantings until the seedling has emerged from the soil. Once the seedling emerges, it needs, ideally, at least four hours of light a day. If your classroom has windows, you can generally expect the following lighting conditions:

- Eastern windows: Receive two to four hours of morning sun.

- Southern windows: Receive full sun during most of the day. Plants can dry out quickly, so watch them carefully.

- Western windows: Generally receive good light for about eight hours a day.

- Northern windows: Receive only diffused light.

**Plant Support:** You may need to support the stems of taller plants such as the kidney bean and sunflower. Prop the plant against a planter stick and gently fasten it with a plastic ring.

The Planting Table in Figure 3-2 provides more information on planting the seeds. Bear in mind that the climate of your classroom will affect the rate of germination. A Monday or Tuesday is the best planting day to try during your first use of the unit.

**Materials**

*For each student*

1 **Planting Cards 1** and **3** (blackline master on pgs. 45–46)

1 **Planting Card 2** (blackline master on pgs. 47–48)

1 plastic bag, 1 liter (1 qt) containing:

    1 clear plastic planter cup, 207 ml (7 oz)

    3 seeds of the same type

    1 plastic spoon

    1 paper towel

*For each group of eight*

1 pail containing moistened potting soil

1 china marker

1 plant mister

1 roll of transparent tape

*For the class*

1 bucket or plastic-lined box or trash can

1 class planter tray and plastic lid, 28 × 53 cm (21 × 11 in)

4 sheets of colored dots (red, blue, white, and yellow)

8 group planter plates (2 red, 2 blue, 2 white, and 2 yellow), 26 cm (10 in)

1 plastic planter cup, 207 ml (7 oz)

  67-lb stock paper for planting cards

34 plant stakes

34 plastic rings

34 planter labels

  Paper towels

  Newspaper

  Bulletin board pushpins or pointed scissors

**Preparation**

1. Copy both sides of the blackline masters for **Planting Cards 1, 2,** and **3** (pgs. 45–48) on the stock paper provided. Make one copy of each for every student. Then, cut the cards apart. Save **Planting Card 3** for Lesson 6. Save the extra copies of **Planting Card 2** for students to use after this lesson.

2. Divide the moistened seed starter into the four pails; each pail should be approximately three-fourths full. Place the rest of the seed starter in the class planter tray (see Figure 3-3).

**Management Tip:** Save the plastic-lined container in which you mixed the potting soil. You will need it in Lesson 4 to mix the terrarium soil.

3. Divide the class into four groups. Each group will plant one of the four kinds of seeds. All members in a group will plant the same kind.

4. Using a bulletin board pushpin or the sharp point of a scissors, punch three small drainage holes into the bottom of each student's planter cup. Follow these steps:

  ■ Assign a dot color to the first group.

  ■ Write a different group member's name on each dot of that color.

  ■ Place one dot about an inch below the top rim of each planter cup.

*Figure 3-3*

*Class planter tray*

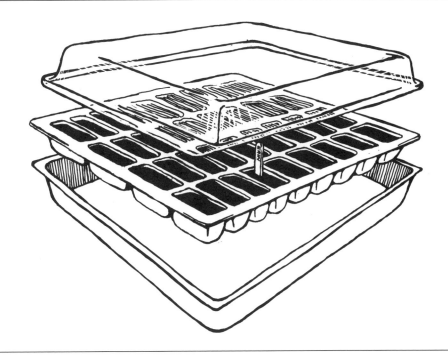

- Repeat this step for the other three groups, using a different-colored dot for each.

- Group the cups according to color.

**Management Tip:** Teachers have found it useful to enlist the help of students in preparing the planter cups a few days before teaching this lesson.

5.  Make individual student planting bags. Write each student's name on a plastic bag. Into each bag put the following items:

    - A planter cup with that student's colored dot on it

    - Three of one type of seed

    - A plastic spoon

    - A paper towel

6.  Set up the planting group areas (see Figure 3-4). Cover them with newspapers.

7.  Have an extra planter cup on hand to demonstrate planting. Identify an accessible classroom storage space for the plantings. (Refer to the **Growing Guidelines** section on pg. 37 for criteria on storage.) Place the eight group planter plates grouped by color in the storage area.

**Procedure**

**Note:** Following is one way to plant the seeds with the whole class at once. Because this is a relatively long lesson, you may want to consider an alternative method, such as setting up a "planting center" and having one group plant at a time.

1.  Invite students to share their previous experiences planting seeds. Ask questions such as, "Have you ever planted seeds before? What did you do? What did you need?"

2.  After the discussion, have students bring a pencil to their planting group's seats.

**Figure 3-4**

*Planting group area*

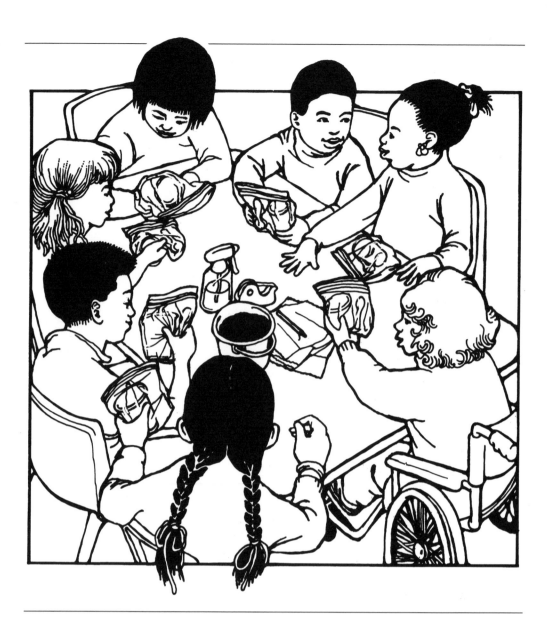

3. Explain to the class the process they will follow.

- There are four different kinds of seeds.

- Each group will plant one of the four kinds of seeds.

- All the members in a group will plant the same kind of seed.

Ask students why they think they will plant two seeds rather than one. If they have no ideas, explain that you will ask again later in the unit. Then follow the instructions below to plant the seeds.

- Use the extra planting cup to show students how to tape one of their seeds to the outside of their cups, below the colored dot (see Figure 3-5).

- Have one or two students at a time take soil from the pail. Have them fill their cups up to the line below the rim. Then ask them to use spoons to smooth the top of the soil.

**Figure 3-5**

*Student planter cup*

- Use your cup, or draw a large cup on the chalkboard, to demonstrate the planting process as you talk students through the following steps:

  - Turn the cup so that the colored dot is facing you.

  - Use the eraser of your pencil to poke two holes about 1 cm (½ in) below the soil if you have the black and white seed, and 2.5 cm (1 in) for the other seeds. Place the holes near the sides of the cup, one to the left of the colored dot and one to the right (see Figure 3-6).

- Place one seed in each hole up against the side of the cup so you can see it. Cover it with soil.

**Figure 3-6**

*Planting*

**Figure 3-7**

*Circling each seed*

- Take turns using the china marker to circle the spot each seed is planted in so you can find it quickly (see Figure 3-7).

- Use the plant mister to moisten the soil thoroughly.

4. Distribute **Planting Card 1** and go over it with the class. Let students know they will observe what happens to their seeds and keep a record in drawings and words. Explain that it is important to date the cards every time they write or draw.

5. Next, have students circle on the card the picture of the seed they planted and write down what they would like to find out about it. On the back of the card, ask them to draw or write in words what they think will happen to the seeds and what they think the seeds will look like (see Figure 3-8).

**Figure 3-8**

*Sample planting cards*

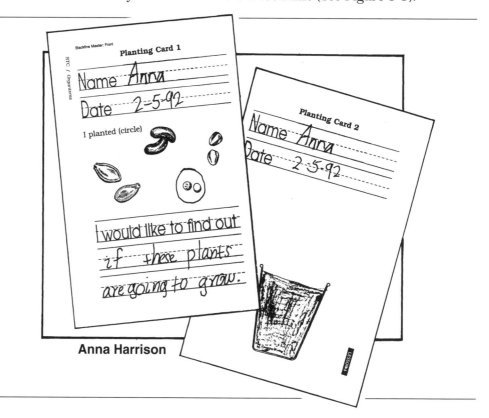

6. Distribute **Planting Card 2.** Ask students to record how the seeds looked today by drawing a picture on this card. When they are finished, have students keep their planting cards in the pocket of a student folder or other container.

7. While the class is working on the planting cards, or later in the day, ask students who brought in seeds from home to plant them in one of the sections of the class planter tray. Write the student's name on a planter label stick and put it next to each planting (Figure 3-3).

8. Finally, plant two of each of the four class seeds in the unused sections of the class planter tray. Label each planted seed by taping one of the seeds on a planter label.

## Final Activities

1. Hold a class discussion on the care of the plantings. Ask questions such as the following:

   ■ What do we need to do to take care of the seeds?

   ■ Where should we put the planted seeds?

   ■ When do you think we should water them?

   Ask students how they think they can tell when a plant needs water. (Past student responses have included, "Water when it's dry," "They need water and sunshine," and "Put them at the window.")

2. Place the clear top on the class planter tray. Have students place the plastic bags over their planter cups, place the planter cups on the matching, color-coded planter trays, and set them in the designated storage area. Keep the plastic bags over the cups until the seedlings emerge. Over the weekends, cover the plantings with plastic bags to keep them moist.

3. Inform students that they will check on their seeds each day and let them know when to do so. Tell them to follow these steps:

   ■ Observe the seed through the cup. Compare it to the seed taped on the outside of the cup.

   ■ If the seed has changed, draw the changes on a new **Planting Card 2** and describe the changes using the sentence starter on the back of the card. Put this new planting card with the other cards.

   ■ Check to see if the planting needs water.

**Management Tip:** When students check their seeds they may not be sure if water is needed. To avoid overwatering, encourage them to ask your opinion.

## Extensions

MATHEMATICS

1. Have students use Unifix™ cubes or strips of paper to measure the plants as they grow. Then have students create individual growth graphs. Use the blackline master **How My Plant Grew** (pg. 49) to have students create a graph of the relative heights of their plants. Choose the units of measurement you would like your class to use.

SCIENCE      ART

2. The subject of seeds and plants has many extension possibilities. Below is a partial list.

   ■ Wrap the seeds first in moist paper towels and place them in plastic sandwich bags to create a "rooterrarium." Hang the bags on a bulletin board so students can observe.

■ Introduce examples of vegetative propagation (growing plants from parts other than seeds) using such things as leaf cuttings, carrot tops, or potatoes.

■ Observe and describe both dried and soaked beans. Open the soaked bean seeds to observe the tiny plant inside.

■ Cook with the class. Use some of the seeds that were planted.

■ Grow alfalfa sprouts or mung bean sprouts to eat at lunch.

■ Grow sponge gardens or "egg-cress-heads." Decorate egg shell halves with faces, fill them with wet cotton, and sprinkle cress seeds on top. Keep the cotton moist and watch the heads grow "hair."

■ Have each student put a sock over one shoe and go outside for a sock walk. The students can sort the seeds they have collected and discuss how they think the seeds travel. Make class graphs of the results.

> **SCIENCE**

3. Make a dirt dessert with your class. You will need the following items:

   1    bag of Oreo® cookies

   2–3  boxes of instant vanilla pudding

        Milk (as needed for the pudding recipe)

   1    container of whipped topping (optional)

   1    bag of gummy worms

   1    25-cm (10-in) plastic flower pot

   1    artificial flower (optional)

Line the flower pot with foil or plastic wrap. Crush the cookies with a rolling pin to make the "dirt." Make the pudding and mix it with the whipped topping. Then decide how you want to layer your dessert. One way is to alternate layers of "dirt," pudding mixture, and gummy worms. Be sure to make the top layer a "dirt" layer. Place an artificial flower in the middle for decoration. Refrigerate this mixture until you are ready to serve it to your class.

**Management Tip:** Lessons 4 and 5 include the setup of the terraria and aquaria. Both are long lessons. You may want to do part of each lesson in the morning and part in the afternoon.

**Note:** Prior to Lesson 4, have the students collect some small rocks, leaf litter, and small twigs for the terraria. You can do this as a class or have students bring materials in from home. You will need enough so that each terrarium (seven for a class of 30) gets a small rock, a layer of leaf litter, and one or two twigs. If you cannot collect leaf litter in your area, garden supply stores often carry leaf mold.

**Planting Card 3**

Name

Date

I found out that

**Planting Card 1**

Name

Date

I planted (circle)

I would like to find out

## Planting Card 2

Name

Date

## Planting Card 2

Name

Date

Today, I observed that

Today, I observed that

**How My Plant Grew**

Name

I planted

| | | | | |
|---|---|---|---|---|
| | | | | |
| Date | Date | Date | Date | Date |
| | | | | |

# Observing Woodland Plants

**Overview and Objectives**

When students planted their seeds, they began to investigate how a plant develops from a seed. Now they broaden their scope and begin to see how a plant flourishes in its natural home. In this lesson, students are introduced to two woodland plants and a terrarium that models the plants' natural home. The class discusses what a woodland is like and then places the plants in a model of a woodland: a terrarium. As students care for the plants in the woodland terrarium, they become aware of the two organisms' needs, as well as their similarities and differences.

- Students observe, draw, and describe two woodland plants: moss and a tree seedling.

- Students discuss what they think the plants need to live.

- Students observe and draw the woodland home, add the plants, and begin a pictorial record of their terrarium.

- Students discuss the similarities and differences between the two woodland plants.

**Background**

The earth is filled with a variety of organisms. The organisms chosen for this unit exemplify life's diversity, in addition to being interesting to children.

As miniature copies of the outside world, terraria are one way to bring the diversity of life on land into the classroom. In this lesson, students observe two woodland plants: moss and a conifer seedling.

Some 400 million years ago, mosses were among the first plants to grow on land. Unlike most other plants, the moss has no true leaves or roots. Instead, these plants grow in clusters and spread like mats over damp ground, trees, dead stumps, and logs. Moss even grows on rock and cement. Students may be interested to know that mosses help break up rocks, prevent erosion, and enrich the soil. The whole plant can soak up water when it rains.

Mosses are seedless and reproduce by spores—tiny one-celled structures. Once the moss becomes established in the terraria, your class may observe stalks with spore cases on their tips (see Figure 4-1).

*Figure 4-1*

*Moss mat and
single moss plant
(magnified)*

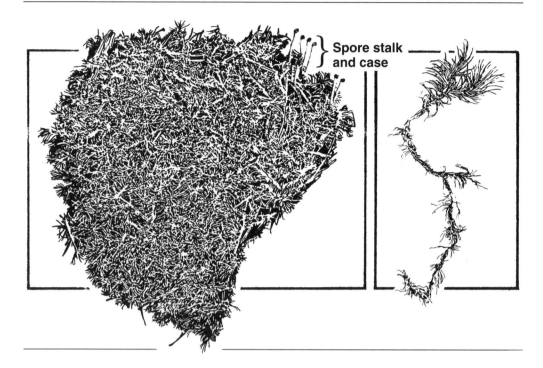

Unlike mosses, **conifers** are seed-producing trees. The seeds of most conifers are produced in cones. Conifers first appeared on the earth about 150 million years ago and include some of the oldest and largest plants on earth. The trees used in this lesson are young plants. Conifers bear narrow leaves called needles in contrast to the broad leaves found on many trees. Unlike the moss, conifers have true leaves and roots. Conifers grow tall and are an important source of lumber.

## Materials

*For each student*

  1  **Record Sheet 4-A: Observing Woodland Plants**
  1  **Record Sheet 4-B: Woodland Picture**
  1  pencil
  1  hand lens

*For every four students*

  1  moss mat
  1  tree seedling
  1  woodland terrarium
  1  plastic spoon
  2  paper towels

*For the class*

  1  plastic tank and lid, 6 liters (1½ gal)
  1  holding container of moss
  1  holding container of tree seedlings
  2  bags of aqua gravel, 2.3 kg (5 lb)
     Woodland terrarium soil, 12 liters (3 gal)
  4  china markers

**Figure 4-2**

*Tree seedling*

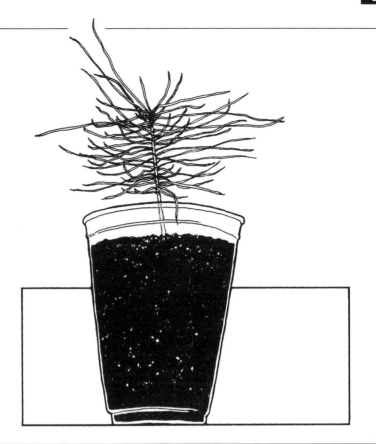

4 plant misters
1 plastic-lined container for mixing soil
2 sheets of newsprint
Leaf litter (loose, decaying leaves)
Small rocks
Twigs

**Preparation**

1. Copy both sides of **Record Sheet 4-A: Observing Woodland Plants** and **4-B: Woodland Picture** for each student.

2. Following the instructions below, set up all the terraria except one, which you will use to demonstrate how a terrarium is set up. Or you may want to have the student teams set up their own terraria as part of the lesson. Read ahead in the **Procedure** to see how you would adapt the setup steps for student teams.

   ■ Put the terrarium soil in your plastic-lined container from Lesson 3.

   ■ It is crucial that the soil be moist but not wet. Add water a cup at a time, mixing evenly. Test the soil by squeezing a small amount each time you add water. The soil should feel moist and clump between your fingers; however, water drops should not come out.

   ■ The terraria will contain three layers (see Figure 4-3). The bottom, or drainage layer, prevents the soil from becoming saturated with water and overgrown with mold. Put a thin layer of gravel, about 1.3 cm (½ in) deep, in each of the terraria.

*Figure 4-3*

*Team terrarium*

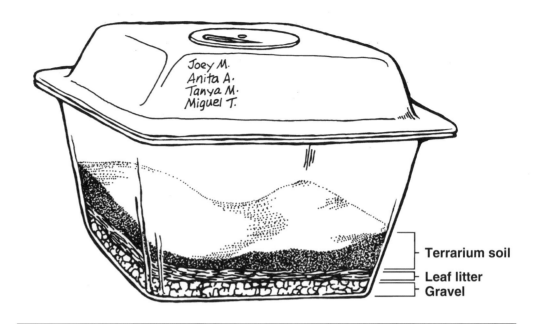

Terrarium soil
Leaf litter
Gravel

- Next, add a thin layer of leaf litter. This will prevent the upper layer of soil from falling into the gravel.

- Finally add about 3.8 to 5 cm (1½ to 2 in) of soil, making the surface slope slightly from rear to front. Create at least one low hill in which to plant the tree.

- Put the plastic lid on the terrarium. Adjust the dial on the top of the lid so that the terrarium is slightly open.

**Management Tip:** Save the leftover soil for Lesson 9. Store it in a covered holding pail to retain moisture.

3. When the plants arrive, refer to Appendix A: Tips on Receiving and Maintaining Live Materials.

4. Divide your class into terrarium teams of four or five. Either you or the students should use a china marker to write the names of the team members in each group on the lid of each terrarium (see Figure 4-3).

**Management Tip:** When forming teams, consider mixing children with different levels of reading, writing, and verbal ability. This will ensure that each team has strengths in each area, since the students are likely to complement and work well with each other. You may also want to arrange the student desks in fours and keep terraria in the middle of each work area for students to observe throughout the day.

5. On the day of the lesson, leave the trees in their cups. Gently separate each of the four moss mats into two pieces. Place a moss mat and a tree seedling on paper towels for each terrarium team.

6. Have these materials at hand so you can demonstrate how to set up a terrarium: tank, soil, gravel, leaf litter, small twigs, and small rocks.

7. If you are not keeping the terraria in the middle of each team's work area, find a classroom space in which to store the terraria, preferably in indirect light. (Full sunlight will overheat the enclosure.) Ideally, the terraria should be accessible to students to observe during their day.

8. Label one sheet of newsprint "Ways the Woodland Plants Are Alike," and the other "Ways the Woodland Plants Are Different."

**Management Tip:** Beginning in this lesson you will use class lists and Venn diagrams to record children's observations. Because these lists and Venn diagrams build on each other, it is important to complete all of them, even though some repetition may be involved. In Lesson 13, you will combine the lists from this lesson with later ones. Read Lesson 13 now to see how they will be used. Some teachers have found it helpful to record student responses on Post-it™ notes, rather than directly onto newsprint. That way, they could easily transfer responses in Lesson 13.

## Procedure

1. Put your students in their terrarium teams and divide the teams into pairs. Ask the class where, in nature, they have seen plants growing. (Other students have said "in grass," "in flower pots," "in gardens," "on farms.") Then explain that today they will look at two plants that grow in woods—moss and a young tree or seedling.

2. Review **Record Sheet 4-A: Observing Woodland Plants** with the class. Show students that they will need to write on both sides. Explain the following items:

   ■ First use the hand lens to observe each plant. Draw it. Then describe it in words or short phrases in the writing space on the front and back of the record sheet. For example, "It's green."

   ■ Each group of four teammates will get one of each plant. With a partner, observe the plant on a paper towel. Then switch with your teammates to observe the second plant.

**Management Tip:** The students will follow a similar observation procedure for each pair of organisms they observe. Take time now to make sure they understand the procedure.

3. Review the observing table from Lesson 2 with students. Emphasize the questions they can now answer about the plants.

4. Distribute the plants, paper towels, and hand lenses.

5. As the teams work, encourage teammates to discuss the plants. To help focus observations, ask students what they notice about the plants' parts. Also help the teams separate a single moss plant to observe closely. After they have worked for a while, make sure teammates switch plants.

6. Have students share their observations of the moss and tree seedling, including observations about both plants' parts.

7. Next, ask students what they think they can do with the plants to keep them alive so that the class can continue to observe them. If students do not suggest planting them, explain that you will help them do so in a miniature woodland called a woodland terrarium.

8. Distribute **Record Sheet 4-B: Woodland Picture,** and show the class the empty tank. Ask students what they think should go in it in order for the plants to live. Explain that they will use the record sheet to keep a record, in drawings and words, of what goes in their team terrarium.

9. Set up the terrarium. Describe each layer and have students draw each layer as you set it up. Ask students to use pencil only.

10. Distribute the team terraria and follow the planting and watering instructions below. Help each team plant a moss mat and tree seedling in its terrarium and use a mister to water each plant. As teams finish planting, have those students draw their plants on Record Sheet 4-B.

■ Help students plant the seedling in the hill you have created in the tank. To remove the seedling from the cup, refer to Figure 4-4.

**Figure 4-4**

*Removing seedling from cup*

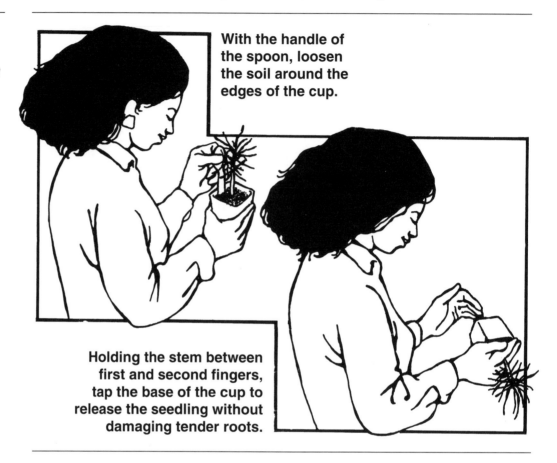

With the handle of the spoon, loosen the soil around the edges of the cup.

Holding the stem between first and second fingers, tap the base of the cup to release the seedling without damaging tender roots.

Be sure the roots of the seedling are completely below the soil line. Gently pat the soil around the seedling. Put more soil around the seedling if needed.

■ Help students plant the moss near or around the seedling. Show them how to scrape a shallow spot for the moss and pat it gently into the soil (see Figure 4-5). Remember, the moss does not have true roots that need to be below the soil line.

■ Show students how to lightly mist the area around the tree. Have them mist the moss directly. Then have them mist the rest of the terrarium lightly.

**Note:** If the plants, soil, light, and humidity are in good balance you may never have to water the terraria again. After a day or so, observe each terrarium. You should be able to notice some moisture condensing on the sides or top of each tank and running back into the soil. If so much condensate occurs that you cannot clearly see through a tank, it is too wet. In that case, adjust the dial on the terrarium lid to open it more and let the tank dry out a bit. If no water condenses, mist the terrarium again.

**Figure 4-5**

*Finished terrarium*

11. Have students add one or two twigs and a small rock to each terrarium. Tell students to place these materials on the side opposite from the plants.

**Management Tip:** If you choose to divide this lesson into two parts, this is one place to stop.

**Final Activities**

1. Give teams a few minutes to observe the two woodland plants in their terrarium and talk with each other about how they think the plants are alike and different.

2. Display the sheets "Ways the Woodland Plants Are Alike" and "Ways the Woodland Plants Are Different." Ask students in what ways they think the moss and conifer seedling are alike. Record their responses. Then ask students in what ways they think the moss is different from the tree. Save these lists for use in later lessons and, if possible, leave them up in the classroom (see Figure 4-6).

3. Discuss with the class how to care for the terraria. Establish a routine to check their moisture level.

4. Have students put the terraria in the designated storage area.

**Extensions**

1. Create a class mural of the woodland terrarium and add to it as the unit progresses. Have the class find out what other plants might live in the woodland and add them to the mural.

*Figure 4-6*

*Sample lists*

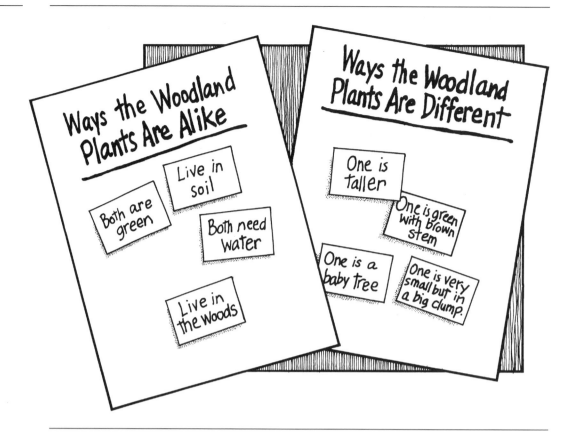

**LANGUAGE ARTS**

2. Use the **Journal Sheet** (blackline master on pg. 65) to help students begin a journal. Provide sentence starters such as, "I was surprised that _____"; "I wonder about _____"; "The most interesting thing I did/observed today was _____." These sheets (see Figure 4-7) can be put together in a book. You can also keep a class journal.

**LANGUAGE ARTS**

3. With the class, read about mosses and trees. For more information, try one of the books in the Bibliography.

**SCIENCE**

4. Set up a class terrarium using plants students have collected locally.

**SCIENCE**   **LANGUAGE ARTS**   **ART**

5. Adopt a tree on the school grounds.

   ■ As a class, list words that describe your tree. How is the tree like the moss and the seedling? How is it different?

   ■ Visit the tree at different times of the school year and ask students to draw it. Bind the drawings in a book and use them to discuss any changes the class has observed over time.

   ■ Read books such as *A Tree Is Nice,* by Janice May Udry (see Bibliography). Have students draw why they think a tree is nice and complete the sentence, "I think a tree is nice because _____."

**Figure 4-7**

*Sample journal sheets*

Anna Harrison

Ann Schellman

**Assessment**

**Record Sheet 4-A: Observing Woodland Plants** introduces a standard format for recording observations. Students will use this same format as they observe the other six organisms throughout the unit. This will enable you to compare earlier and later work (see Figure 4-8).

The **Assessment** section on pg. 30 in Lesson 2 highlighted certain criteria to use when reviewing recorded observations. Also keep in mind the following criteria for assessing individual students:

■ Does the drawing of the organism contain one or more identifying characteristics? For example, in this lesson, a drawing of a tree seedling might have a recognizable stem and long needles and a drawing of the moss might not.

■ Has the student answered any focus questions? For example, in this lesson the students were asked, "What do you notice about the parts of the moss plant?"

■ Is the student's writing becoming more descriptive?

■ Is the student showing interest or enthusiasm toward exploring the characteristics of a living thing?

**Figure 4-8**

*Sample record
sheet*

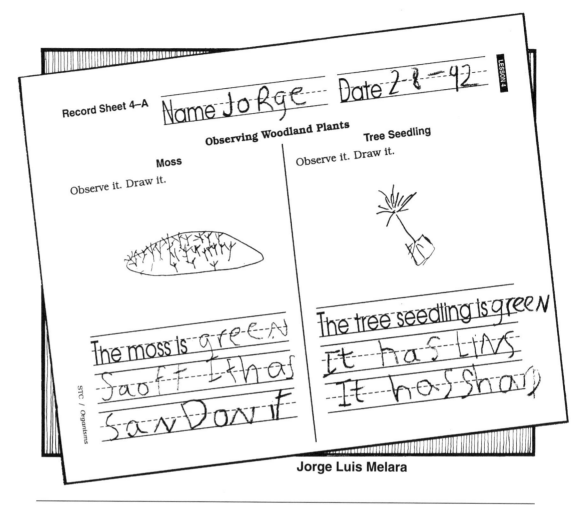

This is the first of several lessons in which students compare two organisms and discuss their similarities and differences. During class discussion in the **Final Activities,** listen for evidence that students are comparing two comparable characteristics. For example, students might say "The tree is sharp and the moss is soft." Conversely, an unlike comparison might be, "The tree is sharp and the moss is brown."

**Note:** Remember, students should be observing their planted seeds every day and recording changes on planting cards.

**Record Sheet 4–A**

Name _____

Date _____

**Observing Woodland Plants**

**Tree Seedling**

Observe it. Draw it.

The tree seedling is _____

**Moss**

Observe it. Draw it.

The moss is _____

# Record Sheet 4–A (continued)

**Moss**

**Tree seedling**

**Record Sheet 4–B**

Name _____

Date _____

**Woodland Picture**

**Record Sheet 4–B** *(continued)*

Name _____ Date _____

**Journal Sheet**

# Observing Freshwater Plants

## Overview and Objectives

Having observed two plants that live on land in Lesson 4, students now broaden their appreciation of the diversity of plant life by observing two plants that live in another environment: fresh water. Through these observations of organisms in two different homes, students begin to realize there are needs basic to all living things and needs specific to different types as well. Applying the process skills introduced in Lesson 4, students once again observe, draw, and describe each freshwater plant to produce a record of their experiences.

■ Students observe, draw, and describe two freshwater plants.

■ Students observe and draw a freshwater home, add two freshwater plants, and begin an ongoing pictorial record of the aquarium.

■ Students discuss how the two freshwater plants are alike and different.

## Background

Plants first evolved in water. Today, water continues to teem with plants, some large and others tiny. Some plants go unnoticed because they live under water. Others, like the water lily, have leaves that float on the water's surface. This lesson introduces students to two freshwater plants that students may not have noticed: *Elodea* and *Cabomba*.

### Elodea

*Elodea* (see Figure 5-1) grows in slow-moving streams, ponds, and backwaters. Its pointed leaves are arranged around the stem in tight whorls of three or more. Small organisms make their homes among the leaves, and snails sometimes lay eggs there.

*Elodea* can float freely near the water's surface or take root at the bottom. Free-floating *Elodea* may send down long, pale roots. While the *Elodea's* stem is somewhat brittle, it can grow up to two feet long, often producing branches as it grows.

Many fish find the *Elodea* good eating. It is a hardy plant—even when stripped of its leaves, *Elodea* still grows. In fact, when broken apart into smaller segments, each piece of *Elodea* can produce roots and grow into a new plant. You and your students may notice small bubbles floating around the *Elodea*. These are bubbles of oxygen produced by the plant.

### *Cabomba*

*Cabomba* (see Figure 5-1) is a delicate, long-stemmed water plant with small branches of fine leaves. Like *Elodea*, it grows naturally in streams and ponds, makes a hardy aquarium plant, and flourishes in strong light. Also like the *Elodea, Cabomba* can either float freely or take root in soil or aquarium gravel.

***Figure 5-1***

Elodea *and* Cabomba

**Materials**

*For each student*

1 **Record Sheet 5-A: Observing Freshwater Plants**
1 **Record Sheet 5-B: Freshwater Picture**
1 pencil
1 hand lens

*For every four students*

1 *Elodea* plant
1 *Cabomba* plant
1 freshwater aquarium, 4 liters (1 gal)
2 paper towels

*For the class*

1 holding pail of *Elodea*
1 holding pail of *Cabomba*
2 newsprint sheets
1 colander
2 bags of aqua gravel, 2.26 kg (5 lb)
  Water, 28 liters (7 gal)
1 china marker
1 plastic aquarium and lid, 4 liters (1 gal)
1 aquarium thermometer
1 bottle of tap water conditioner, 60 ml (2 oz)
1 plastic cup, 207 ml (7 oz)
  Assorted markers
  Newspaper
  White paper

**Preparation**

1. Copy both sides of **Record Sheets 5-A: Observing Freshwater Plants** and **5-B: Freshwater Picture** for each student.

2. Follow the instructions below to set up all but one of the aquarium tanks. You will use the remaining tank for demonstration purposes. Or, as with the terraria, you may want to have student teams set up the aquaria as part of the lesson. Read ahead in the **Procedure** to see how you will adapt these steps for student teams.

■ Keep the same teams you used for the terraria. Use a china marker to write the names of the students on each team near the top rim of each tank. (see Figure 5-2). This will be the front of the aquarium.

**Figure 5-2**

*Layers of aquarium*

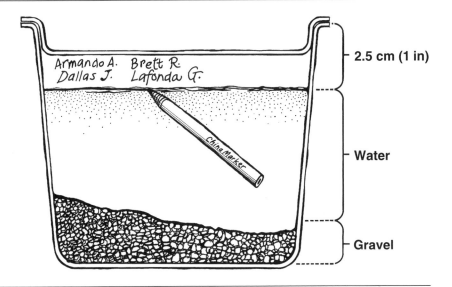

2.5 cm (1 in)

Water

Gravel

■ Now mark a water line 2.5 cm (1 in) below the top of each tank. Water will constantly evaporate, so you will need to add more each week. If the water gets cloudy, it means bacteria are growing and you need to change it.

■ In a pail or colander, rinse the gravel with tap water until the water runs clear. Then rinse each aquarium with warm water. **Do not use soap.**

■ Add two 207-ml (7-oz) cups of gravel to each tank to create a "floor" about 2.5 to 5 cm (1 to 2 in) deep.

■ Slope the gravel so the high end is in the back and the low end is in the front of each tank.

■ Cover the gravel with a piece of blank white paper.

■ Slowly add water to the middle of each tank until you reach the water mark. The water will hit the paper and not disturb the sloped gravel. Remove and throw away or recycle the paper.

■ Add one drop of tap water conditioner to each tank.

■ Store the tanks in your room where they will not be disturbed until you are ready to begin Lesson 5. Always keep the lids on the aquaria. This will protect their contents and slow evaporation.

■ Float the aquarium thermometer in one of the tanks. Water temperature should be between 21°C and 29°C (70°F and 85°F). It may take a day or two for the water temperature to stabilize. If the water becomes too hot or cold, move the aquaria to a new location.

3. When the plants arrive, refer to Appendix A: Tips on Receiving and Maintaining Live Materials.

4. Label one sheet of newsprint "Ways the Freshwater Plants Are Alike" and the other "Ways the Freshwater Plants Are Different."

5. Choose a classroom storage area for the aquaria, preferably in indirect light, away from direct heat and drafts. Make sure the aquaria are accessible to students for daily observation.

   If you are keeping the terraria in the middle of the teams' work areas, place the aquaria there as well. If space is limited, consider rotating between the terraria and aquaria.

6. Have on hand the extra tank, pebbles, and tap water conditioner to demonstrate the aquarium setup.

7. Just before you start the lesson, carefully place a sprig of *Elodea* and *Cabomba* on paper towels for each aquarium team.

8. Cover the team work areas with newspaper.

## Procedure

1. Seat your students in the same teams as in Lesson 4.

2. Review with the students what type of plants they observed in Lesson 4. Explain that today the class will observe two plants that live in freshwater ponds and streams, *Elodea* and *Cabomba*. Write the names of the plants on the chalkboard.

3. Next, distribute **Record Sheet 5-A: Observing Freshwater Plants** and review it with the class. Point out that students used a similar sheet for the tree seedling and moss, and ask them to explain how to use the record sheet. Review any steps that students do not understand. Remind them to use the observing table to help them with their observations.

**Figure 5-3**

*Sample record sheet*

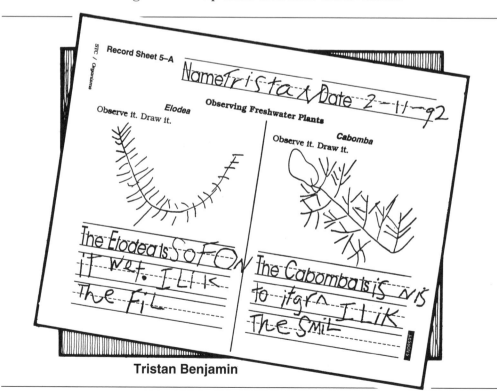

Tristan Benjamin

4. Distribute the plants, paper towels, and hand lenses. Point out to the class which plant is the *Elodea* and which is the *Cabomba*.

5. As the teams work, circulate and encourage them to discuss the plants. To focus observations, ask the class, "What do you notice about the plant stems?" After a few minutes, make sure the teammates switch plants.

6. Have students share their observations of the *Elodea* and *Cabomba*, including what they noticed about the stems.

7. Next, ask students what they might do so that the plants can live and the class can continue to observe them. If students do not suggest it, explain that they will put the plants in a tank that is like a miniature pond or lake: a freshwater aquarium.

8. Now show students the empty tank and ask them what they think should go in it in order for the plants to live. Distribute and review **Record Sheet 5-B: Freshwater Picture** and explain that students will record what goes in their team aquarium, just as they did for the terrarium.

9. Set up your class aquarium. Describe the layer of gravel and layer of water. Have students draw each layer as you set it up.

10. Distribute the team aquaria and help each team add their plants as instructed below. Once a team's aquarium contains the plants, have those students draw their plants into their freshwater picture.

Plant the *Cabomba* (see Figure 5-4).

---

*Figure 5-4*

*Planting* Cabomba

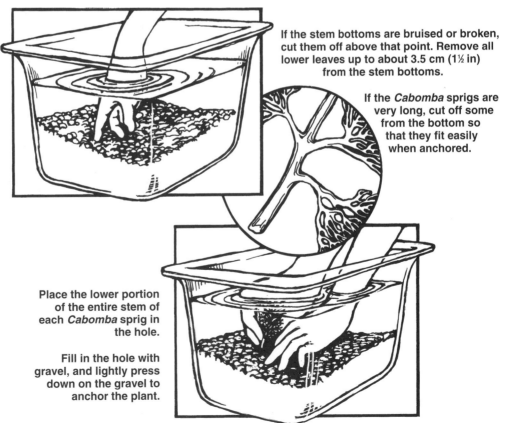

**Poke a hole with your finger in the gravel for the sprigs.**

**If the stem bottoms are bruised or broken, cut them off above that point. Remove all lower leaves up to about 3.5 cm (1½ in) from the stem bottoms.**

**If the *Cabomba* sprigs are very long, cut off some from the bottom so that they fit easily when anchored.**

**Place the lower portion of the entire stem of each *Cabomba* sprig in the hole.**

**Fill in the hole with gravel, and lightly press down on the gravel to anchor the plant.**

Students can add the *Elodea* themselves. Show them how to float sprigs on the water surface (see Figure 5-5).

**Figure 5-5**

*Floating* Elodea

**Final Activities**

1. Give the teams a few minutes to observe the two freshwater plants and to discuss how they think the plants are alike and different.

2. Display the sheets "Ways the Freshwater Plants Are Alike" and "Ways the Freshwater Plants Are Different." Ask the class how they think the *Elodea* and *Cabomba* are like each other. Record their responses (see Figure 5-6). Then ask the class in what ways they think the *Elodea* is different from the *Cabomba*. Save these lists for use in later lessons. If possible hang them near the woodland plants list from Lesson 4.

    **Note:** Once again you may want to write responses on Post-it™ notes for easy transfer in later lessons.

3. Now discuss with the class how to care for the aquaria. Establish a routine to check the water levels.

4. Have students put the record sheets in their student folders.

5. Put the aquaria in the designated storage area if you are not leaving them in the student work areas.

    **Note:** Have students observe the terraria and aquaria even on the days when you are not teaching a lesson from this unit. Other teachers have incorporated this practice into their daily routines by combining observation of the tanks with language arts lessons.

**Figure 5-6**

*Sample student lists*

**Extensions**

> **ART**      **SCIENCE**

1.  Create a class mural of the freshwater aquarium and add to it as the unit progresses. Share a book about pond life with the class (see Bibliography).

> **SCIENCE**      **ART**

2.  Make a list of other freshwater plants students have seen and have them bring in or draw pictures of these plants. Then add them to the class mural.

> **LANGUAGE ARTS**

3.  Ask students to write in their journals about any changes they have observed in the terrarium and aquarium plants. Provide sentence starters such as: "Today I noticed that _____"; "I would like to find out _____."

> **SCIENCE**

4.  Investigate plants that live in salt water. How are they like the freshwater plants and how are they different?

> **SCIENCE**

5.  Start a large (at least 10-gallon) class aquarium. Put a variety of freshwater plants in the aquarium. Discuss with the class how these plants are like the *Elodea* and *Cabomba* and how they are different.

**Record Sheet 5–A**

Name _____

Date _____

## Observing Freshwater Plants

**Elodea**

Observe it. Draw it.

**Cabomba**

Observe it. Draw it.

The Cabomba is _____
_____
_____
_____

The Elodea is _____
_____
_____
_____

## Record Sheet 5–A *(continued)*

**Elodea**

**Cabomba**

LESSON 5

Record Sheet 5–B

Name

Date

Freshwater Picture

STC / *Organisms*

**Record Sheet 5–B** *(continued)*

# How Have Our Seeds Changed?

**Overview and Objectives**

Since Lesson 3, students have been observing and caring for their plants and developing a sense of the needs of living things. Through their observations and experiences, students become more aware that organisms can grow and change. This lesson, which focuses specifically on the changes the seeds have undergone, prepares students for the introduction of their first animal in the next lesson.

- Students observe and discuss the similarities and differences among their plants.

- Students discuss their observations of the changes in seeds they have planted.

- Students create a class story to record their seed planting experiences.

- Students put their planting cards in serial order to create a "Seed Book" that illustrates the beginning life stages of a plant.

**Background**

Throughout their life cycles, organisms grow and change in a variety of ways. Over the past few weeks, for example, the seeds that students planted in Lesson 3 have changed a great deal. In each case, the seed is no longer visible and the plant that has grown from the seed has a visible root system, stem, and leaves. The plants have grown taller and developed more leaves. These changes are recorded on the planting cards on which students have written and drawn observations.

In this lesson, students discover the identity of the plants they have been growing. (Since the seeds are all edible, many students may already know what they are.)

In this lesson's **Final Activities,** your students will verbalize their experience planting and caring for the seeds and you will record them in a class language experience story. Past students have brought up some of the following points:

- There are many kinds of seeds.

- Plants can grow from seeds.

- Seeds contain a tiny plant waiting to grow.

- Seeds need warmth and water to grow.

- Seeds are food for many animals.

- Plants need water, light, and air to grow.

- The root grows first, then the stem and leaves.

**Materials**

*For each student*

 1 pencil

 1 hand lens

 1 student plant (from seed planted in Lesson 3)

   Student's completed planting cards from earlier lessons

 1 copy of **Planting Card 2** (blackline master on pgs. 47–48)

 1 copy of **Planting Card 3** (saved from Lesson 3)

 1 copy of **Taking My Plant Home** (blackline master on pg. 86)

*For the class*

 3 newsprint sheets

 1 "What We Think a Seed Is" list (from Lesson 2)

 1 marker

 1 box of large paper clips

   67-lb stock paper for additional planting cards

**Preparation**

1. Copy the blackline master for **Planting Card 2** (pgs. 47–48), for each student, and have ready the copies of **Planting Card 3** you made in Lesson 3. Also copy both sides of the blackline master **Taking My Plant Home** (pgs. 86–87) for each student.

2. Label one sheet of newsprint "Needs of Plants."

3. Before you begin the lesson, make sure each student has his or her set of planting cards.

**Management Tip:** You may choose to do the **Final Activities** during language arts.

**Procedure**

1. Distribute the hand lenses and a copy of **Planting Card 2** to each student. Have students make one last observation and drawing of their plants. Then ask the class again why they think they planted two seeds. Discuss some reasons, such as that one seed might not have grown.

2. Pair each student with someone who grew a different seed. Have students look at their partners' plants and talk about the ways they think the plants are alike and different. After a few minutes, have students share their ideas with the class and list them on the chalkboard. Past responses include:

 ■ They are green.    ■ They have different shapes.

 ■ They have leaves.    ■ They need soil.

 ■ They need water.    ■ They are different sizes.

3. Focus the students' attention on the class planter tray and then specifically on the pea. Ask students whose plants match it to raise their hands. Then ask them if they know what kind of plant it is. If students are not sure, tell them the plant type. Repeat this for the remaining three seeds.

4. Now distribute **Planting Card 3.** Ask students to use the sentence starter on the card to write about what they discovered by planting their seeds. Have them share ideas with the class.

5. Ask students to put their planting cards in the order that shows the growth of their plants. Give each student a clip to keep the cards together.

6. Ask students who planted seeds from home in the class planter tray to share what they discovered about those seeds.

7. Display the "What We Think a Seed Is" list from Lesson 2. Ask students to point out statements on the list that they now know are true, on the basis of their experiences, and to explain how they know it. Repeat this for those statements they now think are untrue. Have them add new ideas.

8. Display the newsprint titled "Needs of Plants" and ask what students think their plants need to live and grow. Record their thoughts and save the list to revisit throughout the unit.

**Final Activities**

1. Using the guidelines below, have the class write a story about the seeds. Students can refer to their planting cards for help in creating the story.

   ■ Explain to students that you would like to help them write about their experience planting seeds. Once the story is done, other classes can read it or students can read it to their friends or parents.

   ■ Hang the blank newsprint. Explain that students can also look at their set of planting cards as they discuss what they did with the seeds.

   Record on the newsprint what the students share, forming their thoughts into sentences when necessary. Try to have each student contribute at least once. Here are some sample questions to guide the written account:

   ■ What did we do to find out about the four kinds of seeds?

   ■ What did we do to help them grow?

   ■ How did the seeds first change after we planted them?

   ■ How did they continue to change? What grew first? Second?

   ■ What did we do to take care of the plants?

   ■ What did we learn by planting the seeds?

   Below are some ideas on how you can use the class story.

   ■ Copy the story onto different paper. Photocopy it and make an individual book for each student from the class experience story and have students illustrate them (see Figure 6-1). Students can read them with you or independently.

   ■ Have each student draw one picture to illustrate the class story, and make one class book.

   ■ Have your students share their story with another class or with their parents.

2. Give each student a copy of the **Taking My Plant Home** sheet. Ask them to write their names and the names of the seeds they planted on the sheet. Show them the transplanting instructions on the back. Have students take their plants home. You can either continue to care for the class garden or send plants home with the students.

**Management Tip:** After you have sent the plants home with students, you can take down the "What We Think a Seed Is" list.

**Figure 6-1**

*Sample class story*

Mrs. Morse's Class

Grows    Plants

From    Seeds

To help them grow we gave them water and put them in soil. We planted them by the side of the cup so we could watch them.

We planted four different seeds. They were rye, pumpkin, kidney beans, and pea. All but the rye were vegetables.

**Art: Geraldine Decembre**
**Story: Mrs. Morse's First-Grade Class, Glebe Elementary, Arlington, VA**

The root came out first and grew down. The seed got bigger first. After it grew down, it grew up. We call that the stem.

To help them to continue to grow we watered them and we made sure that they had plenty of light. We also gave them love.

Some of the plants grew leaves. Some grew straight. Some grew out.

We learned that a seed is a plant. It can become a vegetable.

## Extensions

ART

1. Have students make covers for their set of planting cards and assemble them into a "Seed Book" (see Figure 6-2 for one way to make books). Keep these books for assessment.

**Figure 6-2**

Sample seed book

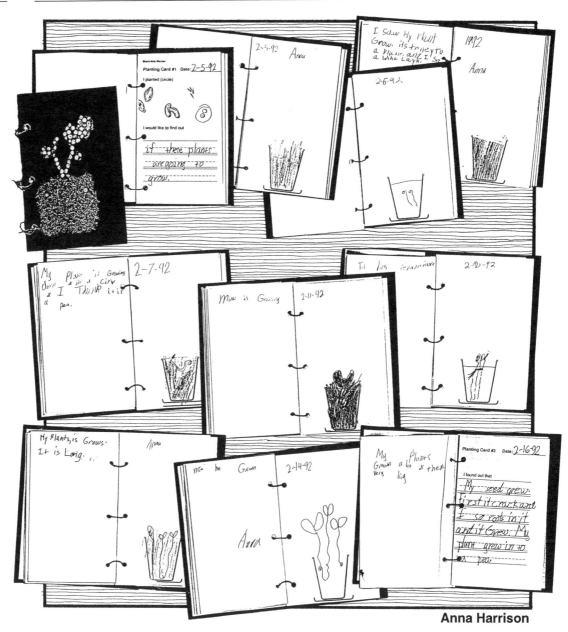

**Anna Harrison**

---

2. Have students bring in fruits and vegetables from home and remove their seeds. Students can sort and classify the seeds. Then make a class graph of the number of seeds removed from each fruit and vegetable.

**SOCIAL STUDIES**   **MATHEMATICS**

3. Create a display of some of the foods we get from seeds. Make a graph of the students' favorite foods. Then make peanut butter with the class.

**LANGUAGE ARTS**

4. There are several good books about seeds to read to the class, such as *A Seed Is a Promise*, by Claire Merrill (see Bibliography). Then have students use drama to illustrate how a seed grows.

5. Read poems about plants from a book such as *Anna's Garden Songs*, by Mary Steele (see Bibliography). Have the student planting groups write poems about their plants.

6. Read stories such as "Johnny Appleseed" and "Jack and the Beanstalk." Have students act out the roles or use stick puppets to dramatize them.

## Assessment

In this lesson, students conclude their observations of growing plants from seeds; however, they will continue to observe and compare plants in the tanks. Below are some areas to focus on at this point.

### Class Discussions

- Were students able to identify some similarities between the plants? For example: color; having leaves, stems, and roots; growing in soil; being a food source; needing water, light, and space.

- Were the students able to identify some differences? For example: size, shape, how fast they grew.

### Class Lists

Analyze student progress by revisiting the "What We Think a Seed Is" list.

- Can students point out statements on the list they now know are true on the basis of experience? Can they explain how they know it?

- Can students point out statements on the list they now think are untrue? Can they explain why?

- What new ideas have students discovered about seeds?

- What plant needs did the class list? For example: water, air, light, a place to live.

- Do students understand that seeds develop into plants?

### Class Language Experience Story

- Did most students participate?

- Were students able to articulate their experiences in response to your focus questions? In particular, did they express an understanding that the seeds and plants change over time?

- Did students offer more information? What kind of information? For example, did they mention the needs of their plants? Ways the plants grew and changed over time? That the roots grew before the stem?

- Did their experiences lead to more questions?

### Seed Books (planting cards)

The seed books provide you with a record of individual student observations on plantings. Consider the following:

- Do the drawings illustrate change in the seed and plant? Was the sequence correct (that is, roots, stem and seed leaves, true leaves)?

- Do the drawings illustrate one or more characteristics of the seed and plant?

- Were the planting cards arranged in the order of the plant's growth?

- Did the student record observations in words? Did the words describe and support the drawings?

- What did the student say he or she learned by planting the seed? Does it reflect actual experiences?

- What questions resulted from the experience of growing a plant from a seed?

Some students may not have written about their plants in the seed books. Try to schedule time to talk with them about the seed books and to ask questions to elicit their experiences.

**Taking My
Plant Home**

# Name

# Date

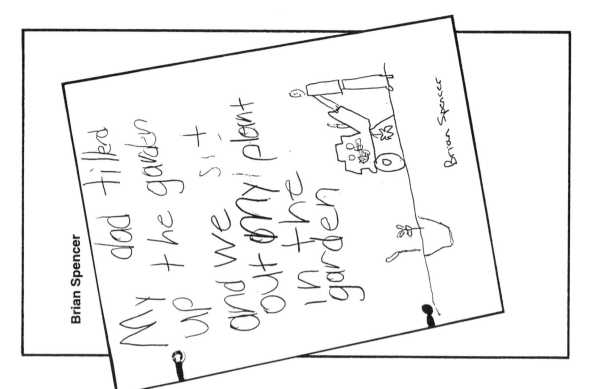

**Brian Spencer**

My dad tilled
My + he garden
up + he sit +
and we sit +
out my plant
in the
garden

Brian Spencer

# Dear

We have been discovering how seeds grow!

My class planted four different seeds.

# I planted

Now it is ready to be transplanted.

Please help me transplant my plant.

Directions are on the next page.

# General Transplanting Instructions

My dad tilled up the garden and we sit out ony plant in the garden

Brian Spencer

*For each plant you need:*

1   15.2 cm (6 in) pot with drainage saucer (unless otherwise indicated in **special requirements** below)

Potting soil

1   spoon
Water
Newspaper

1.   Cover your work area with the newspaper.

2.   Prepare the pot. If you have used the pot before, make sure to wash it out. (Do not use soap.) Be sure the pot has a drainage hole. Fill one-third of the pot with potting soil.

3.   Coax the plant out of the cup with a pencil or similar tool, gently loosening the soil around the plant and taking care not to damage the roots. (Do not grab the stem.) Tip the cup and tap the bottom gently to dislodge the young plant. If the roots are bound tightly, gently loosen them with your fingers.

4.   Place the plant in the middle of the pot and add potting soil to within an inch of the pot's top. Press the soil gently around the plant. Water the pot thoroughly until water comes out the drainage hole. This will help pack the soil around the plant.

The plant will go through a period of shock from being transplanted. Do not worry; it should adjust quickly.

Lighting and other **special requirements** for each plant type are listed below. Eventually, if you want to transplant your plant outdoors, refer to a gardening book. Two recommended books are *The Youth Gardening Book*, by Lynn Ocone and Eve Pranis, and *The Garden Primer*, by Barbara Damrosch.

**Kidney bean:** needs full sun and good drainage

**Pea:** needs partial shade and prefers to be planted in a hanging basket

**Sunflower:** needs full sun

**Pumpkin:** needs sun and a bushel pot to grow well indoors

# Observing Freshwater Snails

**Overview and Objectives**

Students have observed and compared a variety of plants. To expand their understanding of the diversity of life, this lesson introduces the first animal—a freshwater snail. After adding the snail to the same home as the water plants, students will begin to notice that the plants and the snail are coexisting. In later lessons, students will compare the organisms in the aquarium to broaden their understanding that plants and animals have similarities and differences.

■ Students observe, draw, and describe a freshwater snail.

■ Students share their observations in a class discussion.

■ Students discuss what a pond snail needs to live.

**Background**

The animals that students will observe in Lessons 7 through 10 were specifically chosen to exemplify the wide variety of animal life on earth. As they observe the snail, guppy, pill bug, and Bess beetle or millipede, students discover that animals, like plants, need air, water, food, and space to live. Most animals also need some form of shelter. The **Background** sections in the next several lessons provide interesting information on each animal. You may wish to share some of this information with your class. Before you do so, however, be sure to let students formulate their own observations and questions about the animals.

Snails belong to an ancient group of animals called **mollusks,** which includes the octopus, squid, and clam. In fact, some snail fossils date back 500 million years. During that vast stretch of time, snails have become so diverse that today over 80,000 species of snails live on earth.

Snails are **gastropods,** which means "stomach-footed." Snails are invertebrates (they have no bones); however, they do have hard shells that protect their soft bodies. Sticking out from the snail's shell is a foot, made mainly of muscles, for moving. The foot secretes a layer of mucus over which the tender body glides.

The pond snail your students will be observing lives in fresh water, rather than on land. The snail's head is located at the end of its foot and on the head is a set of tentacles (see Figure 7-1). On the tentacles are chemical receptors that detect things such as odors and water quality. At the base of the tentacles are the snail's eyes. Snails can see well at close range (1 m or 3 to 4 ft). The snail is silent and cannot hear. Although the pond snail lives in water, it has lungs and often rises to the water's surface to breathe air.

**Figure 7-1**

*Pond snail
(magnified)*

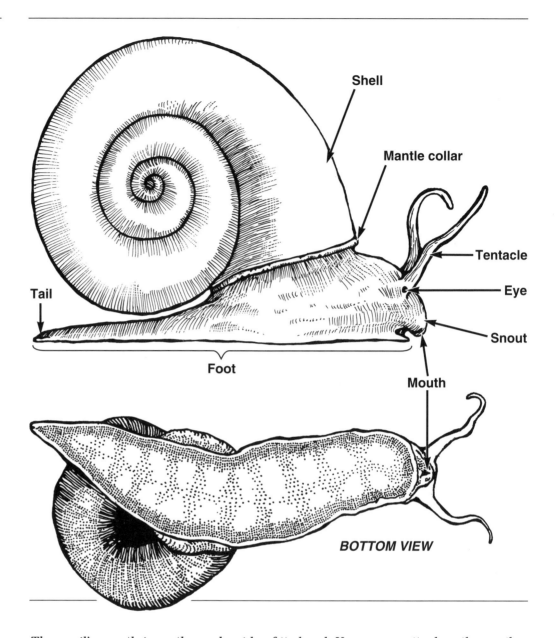

The snail's mouth is on the underside of its head. You can see it when the snail glides along the side of the aquarium. Inside the mouth is a long, flat tongue-like rasp (called the radula), which is covered with rows of tiny, sharp teeth. When the snail eats, it extends the radula and rubs it back and forth against a food, such as a leaf. This filing motion scrapes off small pieces that the snail then pulls into its mouth. Snails are scavengers. They will keep the aquarium relatively clean by eating any algae that build up on the sides. The snail also will eat the plants in the aquarium, plant and animal debris on the bottom and sides of the tank, and the fish food you will give to the guppies.

Most freshwater or land snails are **hermaphrodites,** animals that produce both egg and sperm. A snail's egg, however, must be fertilized by sperm from another snail of its own kind. Before mating, two snails jab each other with a small, sharp, fleshy dart that is part of their female reproductive system. Scientists believe the snail may do this to make sure it has the right partner or to prepare it for mating. About a month after fertilization, the freshwater snails lay their eggs in a jellylike mass on plants or on the sides of the aquarium. Students may see tiny dots in the mass, which are actually tiny developing snails (see Figure 7-2).

*Figure 7-2*

*Small egg mass
(magnified)*

After the snails have been in the aquarium a while, students are likely to discover some egg masses on the sides of the tank. Have students circle the egg masses with the china markers, so they can find them quickly in the future. If the egg masses disappear before any snails hatch, it may be that the guppies you will add in Lesson 8 have eaten them.

As the students continue to observe and care for the snails and other living things, they may develop attachments and be sad if any die. To help students deal with birth and death, read Appendix B, which contains a reprint of an article entitled, "Teaching the Toughest Lesson—About Death." There are also some excellent tradebooks on this subject. See the Bibliography for suggestions.

**Note:** A variety of pond snails will be shipped. Figure 7-1 is a general illustration of a pond snail. Your snails may vary in size, color, and shell shape.

## Materials

*For each student*

   1   **Record Sheet 7-A: Observing Freshwater Animals**
   1   pencil
   1   hand lens

*For each group*

   1   freshwater aquarium, 4 liters (1 gal)
   2   observing cups containing water and a freshwater snail, 266 ml (9 oz)

*For the class*

   3   sheets of newsprint
   1   holding tank with snails and *Elodea*
   3   china markers
      Class observing table (from Lesson 2)
      Markers

## Preparation

1. Before the snails arrive, remember to alert your school's office that they are coming. When they arrive, open the box immediately and follow the instructions in Appendix A: Tips on Receiving and Maintaining Live Materials.

2. Just before the lesson, add about one-third of a cup of water to two observing cups per team. Put one snail in each cup. Keep extra snails in the holding pail. If any die, simply replace them.

3. Use one sheet of newsprint to set up a snail Venn diagram (see Figure 7-3). For general information on Venn diagrams, refer to pg. 8 of Teaching *Organisms*.

4. Label the second sheet of newsprint "What We Would Like to Find Out about Pond Snails."

**Figure 7-3**

*Snail Venn diagram*

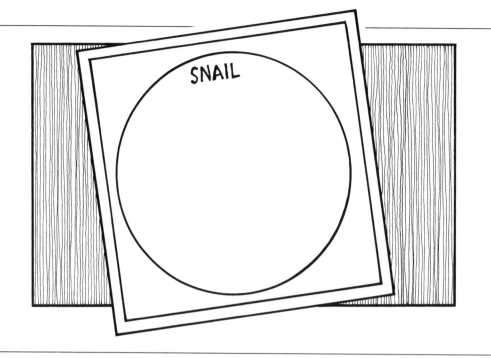

5. Arrange the class into freshwater aquarium teams.

**Management Tip:** You may want to discuss some rules on keeping living things in the classroom. For example: "Look but don't touch, unless the teacher says it is all right."

**Procedure**

1. Ask students what animals they think might live in freshwater ponds, streams, and lakes.

2. Let students know that today they will observe an animal that lives in fresh water with *Elodea* and *Cabomba*, a freshwater snail. Then distribute **Record Sheet 7-A: Observing Freshwater Animals** and review it with the class.

3. Distribute two observing cups with snails to each team. Pair partners within each team as you go.

4. Then have students leave the cups undisturbed on the desk and observe the snails. After a minute or two, do the following:

   ■ Display the newsprint labeled "What We Would Like to Find Out about Pond Snails."

   ■ Ask, "What would you like to find out about the pond snail?"

   ■ Record the questions on the newsprint.

   ■ Ask, "Which questions might we answer by observing the snails today?" Place a check next to these questions.

   ■ If the list does not include the question "How does the snail move?" add it.

5. Explain the process students will follow:

   ■ With your partner(s), use the hand lenses to observe the snail in its cup. Discuss your observations.

   ■ Use the class observing table to help you describe the snail. Then see if you can answer one or two questions that have been checked on the chalkboard.

6. Circulate to be sure each student is both drawing and describing the snail. After a few minutes, you may gently take the snail out of each cup. If a snail is attached to the cup, be sure to move it slowly to avoid damaging it. Let each student hold the snail for a minute or two. Then encourage students to complete their snail descriptions after holding it.

7. Place each team's aquarium at its work area. Gently put the snails into the aquaria. Let the students observe them there.

8. After a few minutes, have students share their snail observations. Record these on the left side of the circle in the snail Venn diagram. Explain that the circle represents the snail. Observations that describe the snail go inside the circle (see Figure 7-4). Observations that do not describe the snail go outside the circle. To get students started, ask questions such as:

   ■ What did you find out about the snail?

   ■ What are some words that describe the snail?

   ■ What is the snail's body like?

   ■ What did you find out about the way the snail moves?

   ■ What did the snail do while you were observing it?

*Figure 7-4*

*Sample snail Venn diagram*

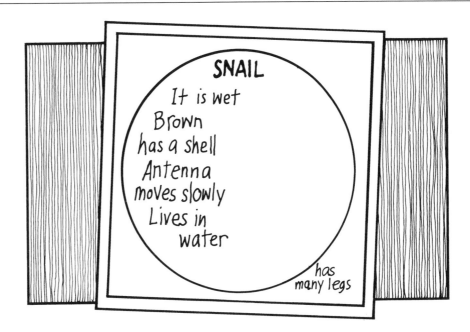

**Management Tip:** If possible, keep the animal Venn diagrams posted so students can add new observations during the day. Keep a supply of paper "idea strips" for students to add to the diagram.

9. Once again, ask students to take a look at their questions on the newsprint. Can they now answer more of the questions? Circle those questions answered as a result of today's observations. Next, add any new observations to the snail Venn diagram.

10. If some questions remain unanswered, let students know they will be able to observe the snails in the aquaria throughout the rest of the unit.

**Final Activities**

1.  Focus students on the class observing table and remind them that it contains their questions about seeds and plants. Then ask if there are any questions they have answered about their snail that are not already on the table. Attach the blank sheet of newsprint and add the new questions (see Figure 7-5).

**Figure 7-5**

*Adding questions to the observing table*

2.  Ask the class, "What do you think the snail needs to live?" Explain that students will observe the snails in the aquaria to discover what they eat and whether they have what they need to live.

3.  If you are not keeping the aquaria on the student's desks, return the aquaria to their storage area. Empty the observing cups to use them again for the guppies in Lesson 8. Also save the snail Venn diagram for Lesson 8. Students will use **Record Sheet 7-A** again in Lesson 8.

**Extensions**

LANGUAGE ARTS

1.  Read *Snail's Spell*, by Joanne Ryder (see Bibliography). Then have students act out the passages describing what it feels like to be a land snail and have them act out the role of a water snail.

LANGUAGE ARTS

2.  You and your class can learn more about snails by reading books such as *Snail*, by Jens Olesen (see Bibliography).

SCIENCE     LANGUAGE ARTS     ART

3.  Copy the blackline master of the snail outline (pg. 228). Have students make stuffed paper snails.

Following are the steps to create a stuffed snail:

- Have students cut out the snail outline or draw their own outline and cut it out.

- Place the cutout snail onto another piece of paper. Staple or glue it there. Be sure to leave an opening for stuffing.

- Have students cut around the outline of the snail.

- After they have closely observed the real snail, have students use construction paper to add anatomical details to their models (for example, eyes and antennae).

- Have students color or paint their snail models.

- Have students use scrap paper to gently stuff the animal. Help students staple the opening shut.

You can use your stuffed snails in a variety of ways:

- Mobiles using words to describe the animal

- A catalyst for creative writing about the snail

- A puppet to dramatize students' snail observations

- Covers for snail-shaped books

- A general snail outline to which students can add characteristics of different snails they learn about

Display the snails on a class board and have students discuss the differences and similarities among the various types of snails.

> **ART**

4. Do snail art with your class. For example:

- Make paper snails. Have the students form paper strips of three or four different lengths into circles. Then paste the circles inside one another to form the snail's shell. Cut a separate strip for the snail's body and paste the shell in the middle of the body. Add pipe cleaners for antennae.

- Make fingerprint snails. Have students make a number of fingerprints from a stamp pad. Have them turn these into snails and draw in the snails' habitats.

**Assessment**

For your information, Figure 7-6 shows a sample of **Record Sheet 7-A: Observing Freshwater Animals.**

- Students' observations of the four animals in this unit will range in content. In general, students will focus on describing the animals by color, size, and one or two distinguishing characteristics. Some students may eventually include some of the animals' needs or behaviors.

- Be sure students have time for spontaneous observations. Adding animals to the tanks may spark a lot of discussion among students, providing a natural opportunity for small group or whole class discussions. You may also want to follow up these discussions with an art, writing, or drama activity.

**Figure 7-6**

*Sample record
sheet*

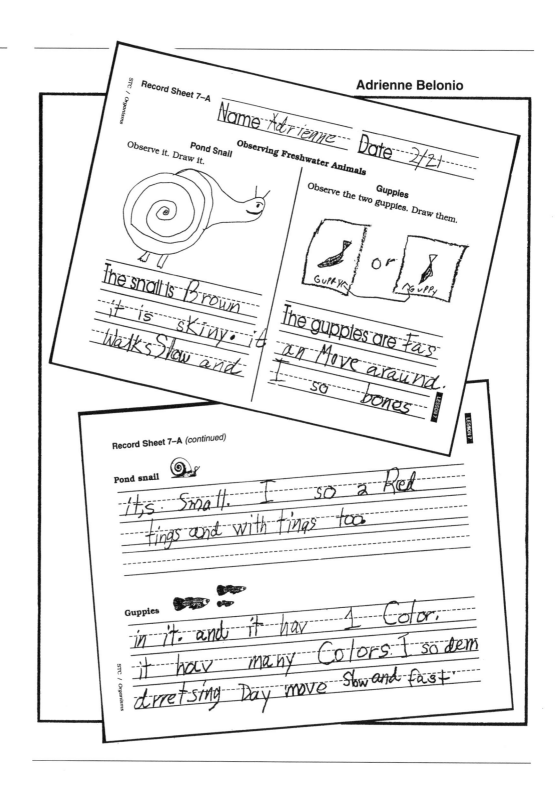

**Management Tip:** If you need to maintain the aquaria unattended for longer than four days, do the following:

- Remove the aquaria from extreme cold or drafts. If the heat will be turned off, find a very warm place in the room or send the aquaria home with students.

- To feed the fish over more than four days, do not add a large supply of the usual fish flake food. This will foul the tank. Instead, use time-release food tablets, found in most pet stores.

**Notes**

Preview Lessons 11 and 12 at this time. Some teachers have found that they would have liked to have done the observing and writing activities in these lessons earlier in the unit.

Bess beetles and millipedes are difficult to **culture,** or raise, in a laboratory. They can be collected in the wild only during certain seasons. In addition, because it is important to maintain nature's ecological balance, they cannot be overcollected. Therefore, the kit supplies fewer Bess beetles and millipedes than pill bugs, snails, and guppies. In Lesson 10 you will receive either eight Bess beetles or eight millipedes (one per terrarium team) along with the shipment of pill bugs.

**LESSON 7**

Name _____

Date _____

## Observing Freshwater Animals

### Pond Snail

Observe it. Draw it.

### Guppies

Observe the two guppies. Draw them.

The snail is _____

The guppies are _____

# Record Sheet 7–A (continued)

**Pond snail**

**Guppies**

# Observing Guppies: How Do They Compare with the Snails?

**Overview and Objectives**

In this lesson, students are introduced to a second freshwater animal, the guppy. After adding guppies to the aquarium, students will begin to notice that not only do plants coexist with animals but also that animals coexist with other animals in the same environment. By observing a pair of male and female guppies, students are introduced to the similarities and differences within a single organism.

- Students observe, draw, and describe a male and female guppy.

- Students share their observations, discussing the similarities and differences between the guppies.

- Students use a class Venn diagram to identify and discuss the similarities and differences between the guppy and snail.

- Students discuss what guppies need to live.

**Background**

In almost every natural body of water, there are fish. Fish appeared on the earth about 400 million years ago. Today, more than 25,000 kinds of fish live throughout the world. They thrive deep in the sea, in mountain lakes, in rivers and streams, and even in 43°C (110°F) water holes in the desert. There are a wide variety of fish; some are as tiny as a fingernail while others are as long as a bus. Fish exhibit these characteristics:

- Fish are **vertebrates** (have a backbone). Most fish also have jaws.

- Most fish are covered with scales.

- Fish have fins. The tail fin is used for power, and the pectoral fins steer. The dorsal fin on the back provides stability.

- Fish have a well-developed sense of sight, touch, smell, taste, and hearing.

- Fish have a special sensory organ, a **lateral line** that runs the length of the body and detects any movement of water around the fish.

- Most fish have swim bladders that provide buoyancy.

- Most fish pump water through their mouths and over their gills to breathe under water.

Guppies are active, hardy fish that thrive in a wide range of conditions. Guppies originated in the West Indies and South America. They now occur in warm climates over much of the world. Because they eat many young mosquitos, these fish have earned the appreciation of humans.

In this unit, the guppy is the only animal that is introduced to students in male-female pairs; the intent is to provide students with a likely opportunity to observe reproduction. Unlike most other fish, male guppies fertilize the females internally, and the females bear live young. These distinctive characteristics give children the opportunity to witness the birth of organisms and to observe that some traits are passed from parent to offspring. In addition, by observing a male and female guppy, the class can see that distinct differences can occur within one species of organism (see Figure 8-1).

**Figure 8-1**

Guppies

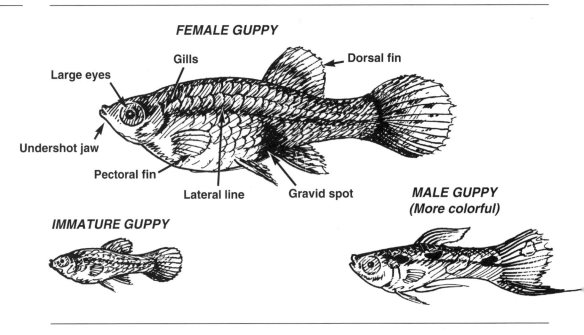

The male guppy is the smaller of the two, growing to a length of 3 cm (about 1¼ in). His body is slim with pointy fins. A colorful fish, the male guppy has shiny orange, pink, black, blue, or white markings. He has a large, handsome tail that he often fans open for display like a peacock, especially when courting the female.

The female guppy is much larger than the male and can grow up to 6 cm (2½ in) long. She is a drab, grayish green. Her fins and tail are rounded, as is her body. At three months of age, the female can start to have babies. When the female is pregnant, her abdomen becomes very swollen, and a black gravid spot (indicating pregnancy) appears on each side of her body just above the pelvic fin.

Guppies are quite prolific; in fact, the female can give birth to up to 50 babies at a time. The babies are born alive and fully formed, and look much like adults (baby guppies of both sexes resemble adult females more than males in that they are rounded and a dull color). The babies are more transparent than the adults. Less than 1 cm (¼ in) long at birth, they become full grown in about eight months.

**Materials**

*For each student*

1 **Record Sheet 7-A: Observing Freshwater Animals** (from Lesson 7)
1 pencil
1 hand lens
  Crayons

*For the group*

   1   freshwater aquarium, 4 liters (1 gal)

   1   observing cup containing water and a male guppy, 266 ml (9 oz)

   1   observing cup containing water and a female guppy, 266 ml (9 oz)

*For the class*

   2   sheets of newsprint

   1   snail Venn diagram (from Lesson 7)

   1   holding tank with guppies

   1   container of fish food

   2   dip nets, 5 cm (2 in)

   1   empty holding pail

   1   roll of tape

   1   class observing table (from Lesson 7)

      Assorted colored felt markers

## Preparation

1. Guppies are more fragile than the other organisms in this unit. Be sure to ask the front office to tell you as soon as they arrive. Open the box immediately and refer to Appendix A.

2. Just before the lesson, fill two observing cups per team with water from the holding tank. Put a male guppy in one cup and a female in the other (see Figure 8-2). Leave the extra guppies in the holding tank to replace any that may die (see Appendix B for more information on the possible death of the animals).

**Figure 8-2**

*Netting and
releasing the guppy*

3. Be sure each student has his or her copy of **Record Sheet 7-A: Observing Freshwater Animals.**

4. On a sheet of newsprint, prepare the guppy Venn diagram sheet just as you did the snail Venn diagram in Lesson 7.

5. Label the second sheet of newsprint "What We Would Like to Find Out about Guppies."

6. In Step 2 of the **Final Activities** you will talk with the class about what guppies eat. Try to have students feed the fish at roughly the same time each day. (For the first feeding, it is important that students take some time for observation.) The guppies need just a small pinch of food and should finish it within five minutes. If food is left floating, reduce the amount.

   **Note:** Do not tell students the two guppies are of different sexes; let them discover this themselves through observing.

**Procedure**

1. Explain that today the class will observe an organism that lives in fresh water with the snail: the guppy. Ask if any students have had fish for pets and allow time for them to share experiences.

2. Now ask students to look at their copies of **Record Sheet 7-A: Observing Freshwater Animals,** and explain that today they will observe, draw, and describe guppies. Also explain that each team will take turns observing two guppies and that students will draw both fish on their record sheets.

3. Distribute the observing cups. Pairing partners as you go, make sure each team receives a male and a female guppy.

4. Have students leave the cups undisturbed on the desks and observe the guppies. After a minute or two, do the following:

   ■ Display the newsprint labeled "What We Would Like to Find Out about Guppies."

   ■ Ask, "What would you like to find out about the guppy?"

   ■ Record the questions on the newsprint.

   ■ Ask, "Which questions might we answer by observing the fish today?" Put a check next to these.

   ■ If the list does not contain a question about how guppies move, add, "What parts of the guppy's body does it use to move?"

   ■ Show students the place on the record sheet where they can record observations and draw the two guppies.

   ■ See if you can answer a checked-off question from the class list.

5. Remind students to refer to the class observing table for help in describing. Also let pairs of students know that you will tell them when to switch guppies within their teams.

6. When students have finished observing the first guppy, ask the pairs within each team to switch cups. Ask students to draw the second guppy and to add any new observations.

7. Put each team's freshwater aquarium at its work area. Have students gently float the observing cups in the aquarium for about 15 minutes (see Figure 8-3). Explain that this will help the guppies get used to the water temperature in the tank. While the cups are floating, move to the next step.

**Figure 8-3**

*Floating the
observing cups*

8. Have students share their guppy observations (see Figure 8-4). Record them on the right side of the circle in the guppy Venn diagram you prepared earlier and explain that this circle represents the guppies. To get students started, ask questions such as the following:

- What did you find out about the guppies?

- What are some words that describe the guppies?

- What are the guppies' bodies like?

- What did you find out about which body parts the guppies use to move?

- What did the guppies do while you were observing them?

- Why do you think one guppy is more colorful than the other?

Then ask students to discuss ways the guppies are different from each other. Follow up by having the students share why they think there are differences among animals of the same kind.

**Figure 8-4**

*Sample guppy
Venn diagram*

9. Next have students look again at their questions on the newsprint. Ask if they can answer any more of the questions and circle those they have answered as a result of today's observations. Then add any new observations to the guppy Venn diagram.

10. If some questions remain, let students know that they will be able to observe the guppies in the aquaria throughout the rest of the unit.

11. Now add the guppies to the aquaria according to the following instructions:

   ■ Carefully pour one of the cups over a dip net (and over the empty holding pail) and net the guppy.

   ■ Quickly place the net in the aquarium and release the guppy. Gently reverse the net if the guppy does not swim out on its own.

   ■ Repeat this process for the second cup and the remaining aquaria. Ask students to observe the guppies in the aquaria as you circulate.

**Management Tip:** If you choose to divide this lesson into two parts, this is a logical stopping point.

**Final Activities**

1. Display the snail Venn diagram from Lesson 7 next to the guppy Venn diagram. Explain that these circles contain students' observations of the snail and guppy. The class will use these circles to talk about how the two animals are alike and how they are different. Now follow the instructions below and in Figure 8-5 to use the Venn diagram to compare the snail and the guppy.

   ■ Move the two diagrams so that they overlap, creating an intersection. Use a marker to outline the center space.

   ■ Explain that in the center space where the two circles overlap, you will use a different colored marker to list the ways the snail and guppy are alike. To refresh students' memories, read aloud their snail observations.

   ■ Have the class look at the observations for the snail and the guppy to see if any are true for both animals. As you write these observations in the center space, cross them out in the outer part of the circles. Remember, while the words may not match exactly, the concepts should be similar. Show the class that the center space contains statements that are true for both the snail and the guppy.

   ■ To help students think of some other ways the snail and guppy are alike, ask, "What do both the snail and guppy do?" "How do they act in the aquarium?" Add new ideas to the intersection. Past students have added such ideas as "They both eat and move" and "They both need water."

   ■ To highlight ways in which the snail and guppy differ, focus students on the observations that have not been crossed out.

2. Ask the class, "What do you think the guppy needs to live?" Explain that once a day, you will give students some food to feed the fish. Then, students will observe the aquaria to see what else the guppies eat and if they have what they need to live.

3. Make sure the two circles are taped together so you can save the snail and guppy Venn diagram for use in Lesson 14.

**Figure 8-5**

*Comparing the snail and the guppy*

Move the two sheets together so that the circles overlap, creating an intersecting space. Tape the sheets together.

Trace over any circle parts and words that are covered. This will outline the intersecting center space.

4. If you are not keeping the aquaria on students' desks, return the aquaria to their storage area. Empty the observing cups. You will use them again for the pill bugs in Lesson 9.

**Note:** Now that the freshwater habitats are set up, students will continue to observe the organisms informally. To stimulate students' curiosity, ask questions such as the following:

- What do the animals do all day?

- When are they most active? Least active?

- How do the animals use the plants?

- Where in the habitats do the animals spend the most time?

- What changes do you observe happening in the habitat?

## Extensions

**LANGUAGE ARTS**

1. Read a fish story such as *A Million Fish . . . More or Less,* by Patricia C. McKissack (see Bibliography).

**ART**    **LANGUAGE ARTS**

2. Copy the blackline master of the guppy outline on pg. 229. Have students make stuffed paper fish. Then try one of the ideas listed in Extension 3 of Lesson 7 (pgs. 94–95).

**ART**

3. Make fish prints with your class. Flat fish such as flounder work best. Have students follow these steps:

- Rinse the flounder and pat it dry.

- Using acrylics, paint one side of the fish.

- To transfer the impression, place a piece of white drawing paper over the fish and gently press on the paper, or flip the fish onto the paper and press on the fish.

**SOCIAL STUDIES**

4. Highlight the importance of fish as a food source by having a fish luncheon, serving a few types of fish found in your area. Make a class graph representing the students' favorite edible fish.

**SCIENCE**    **LANGUAGE ARTS**

5. Take a class trip to a local fish hatchery. Have students compare the guppy with other fish. Then have students write and draw about their experience at the hatchery.

## Assessment

This is the first time in the unit that students compare two animals. When reviewing the class discussion and Venn diagrams, consider the following items:

- What comparisons between the animals do students make?

- Are students becoming aware that most organisms have basic and specific needs?

- Can students identify additional ways in which animals are alike? For example: They are able to move.

Now that students are maintaining a variety of organisms in the classroom, look for evidence of the following:

- The ability to care for living organisms

- The development of positive attitudes toward different forms of life

- The development of sensitivity to the needs of living things

- A growing awareness of the diversity of life

**Management Tip:** Your class will need to collect at least eight green leaves for use in Lesson 9. If there are no leaves available, use lettuce.

# Observing Pill Bugs

**Overview and Objectives**

So far, students have observed animals that live in a water environment. Now they examine a land animal, the pill bug, and add it to their woodland environment. Following the same process used in Lessons 7 and 8, students discover that animals, just like plants, have a number of different characteristics. Lessons 9 and 10 continue to reinforce students' observation skills and use of descriptive language.

■ Students observe, draw, and describe a land animal: the pill bug.

■ Students share their observations of the pill bug in a class discussion.

■ Students discuss what a pill bug needs to live.

**Background**

More animals populate the land than the water. The largest and most varied group of animals, the **arthropods** (meaning jointed legs), comprises insects, centipedes and millipedes, spiders and crustaceans (shrimp, crabs, and isopods).

Water bug, wood louse, slater, potato bug, and roly poly are just some of the names people call pill bugs—the crusty little animals the students observe in this lesson. While the pill bug may resemble a cross between an armadillo and an insect, it is in fact a crustacean. As such, it is a close relative of the lobster, crab, and shrimp. Pill bugs are part of the crustacean group called **isopods,** meaning "equal legs." Although most isopods live in water, the pill bug lives in damp earth or sand. Like its aquatic relatives, the pill bug needs moisture at all times, because it breathes through gills.

The pill bug has a small head with long antennae and a short, wide segmented body with 14 legs (if a pill bug has only 12 legs it is very young). Lobsters, crabs, and shrimp have eyes which are mounted on movable stalks, but the pill bug's eyes are on the sides of its head (see Figure 9-1).

Lacking backbones, pill bugs have a protective **exoskeleton** or outer skeleton. This shell is made of **chitin,** a hard substance that is similar to the material in your fingernails. Because the exoskeleton cannot expand, the pill bug must shed, or **molt,** in order to grow. The pill bug molts half of its exoskeleton at a time, usually the front half first. If the pill bug is dark gray or black, then it has molted a while ago. If it is light gray or brown, it has just molted or is in the process of molting.

The pill bug's shape enables it to squeeze under things, and it is most often found under wood, bark, or leaves. The pill bug feeds on both live and dead plant material. Pill bugs have strong jaws that can tear into stems and roots;

**Figure 9-1**

Pill bug

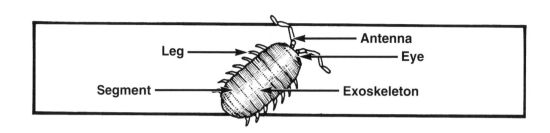

Leg — Antenna — Eye — Segment — Exoskeleton

therefore, it is natural for them to disturb the moss and seedling in the terrarium. Pill bugs' natural predators are birds, lizards, and spiders. A pill bug's defense is to roll into a ball to protect its softer underside (see Figure 9-2). Pill bugs are also able to move quickly.

**Figure 9-2**

The pill bug rolls up into a ball for protection.

If you notice a bulging pill bug, you may have a pregnant female. She carries up to 200 eggs in a brood pouch under the front end of her body. The eggs hatch in the pouch, where the babies remain for about three weeks. Immediately after the young emerge from the pouch, they are small and very pale and may be hard for the children to see.

## Materials

*For each student*

   1  **Record Sheet 9-A: Observing Woodland Animals**
   1  pencil
   1  hand lens

*For each group*

   2  observing cups, each containing soil, a leaf, and a pill bug, 266 ml (9 oz)
   2  lids for plastic cups
   1  woodland terrarium, 6 liters (1½ gal)

*For the class*

   2  sheets of newsprint
   1  holding pail containing pill bugs
   8  green leaves (or lettuce)
      Markers

## Preparation

1. Copy **Record Sheet 9A: Observing Woodland Animals.**

2. Prepare a pill bug Venn diagram on a sheet of newsprint.

3. When the pill bugs arrive, refer to Appendix A.

4. Just before the lesson, prepare two observing cups for each terrarium team with a thin layer of moist soil from the pill bug holding pail. Put one pill bug and one green leaf or piece of lettuce in each cup. Then cover both cups with lids.

5. Label the second sheet of newsprint "What We Would Like to Find Out about Pill Bugs."

6. Arrange the class in their terrarium teams.

7. In Step 2 of the **Final Activities,** you will talk with the class about what the pill bugs need to live. Simply by maintaining the terrarium as usual, you will supply the pill bug with most of its needs. Be sure there are leaf litter, twigs, and bark in each terrarium. Placing a green leaf or lettuce near the bark and twigs may force the pill bugs to come out to feed. Try to keep the twigs on the opposite side of the tank from the pine and moss so that the pill bugs disturb the plants as little as possible.

**Procedure**

1. Ask students what animals they think may live in the woods. Then let them know that today they will observe an animal that can live in the woods with the tree seedling and moss: a pill bug.

2. Hand out and review **Record Sheet 9-A: Observing Woodland Animals.** Point out that it is just like the record sheet students used to observe the freshwater animals.

3. Hand out two observing cups to each team, pairing partners as you go.

4. Have students leave the cups undisturbed on their desks and observe the pill bugs. After students have observed the pill bugs for several minutes, do the following:

   ■ Display the newsprint labeled "What We Would Like to Find Out about Pill Bugs."

   ■ Ask, "What would you like to find out about the pill bug?"

   ■ Record the questions on the newsprint.

   ■ Ask, "Which questions might we answer by observing the pill bugs today?" Put a check next to these questions.

   ■ If the list of questions does not contain "Where are the eyes?" add it.

   ■ See if students can answer one or two checked questions.

   ■ Again, point out that students need to record what they find out about the pill bug's eyes on the back of the record sheet.

   ■ Explain that they will have to observe very closely.

5. As students observe the pill bugs, tell them to follow these steps:

   ■ With a partner, use the hand lenses to observe the pill bug in its cup and discuss observations. You can pick up the cup, but do not let the pill bug out of the cup—it moves very quickly.

   ■ Use the class observing table to help describe the pill bug. See if you can answer one or two questions that have been checked on the newsprint.

6. After students have observed a few minutes, let interested students gently touch the pill bug while it is in the cup. Ask children what happens when they touch the pill bug.

7. Put each team's terrarium at its work area. Have students gently tip the observing cups to put the pill bugs into the terraria and observe them for a few minutes. Give each team a green leaf or piece of lettuce to put near the bark or twigs.

8. As students share their pill bug observations, record them on the left side of the pill bug Venn diagram you prepared earlier (see Figure 9-3). To get students started, ask questions such as the following:

   ■ What did you find out about the pill bug?

   ■ What are some words to describe the pill bug?

   ■ What is its body like?

   ■ Where are the pill bug's eyes?

   ■ What did the pill bug do while you were observing it?

*Figure 9-3*

*Sample pill bug Venn diagram*

9. Now have students look again at their questions on the newsprint. Ask if they can answer any of their questions and circle those they answer based on today's observations. Then add any new observations to the pill bug Venn diagram.

10. If some questions remain unanswered, tell students they will be able to observe the pill bug in the terrarium throughout the rest of the unit.

   **Note:** Refer to Appendix A for tips on maintaining the pill bugs in the classroom over time.

**Final Activities**

1. Focus attention on the class observing table. Now that students have observed three different animals, ask them if there are any questions they have answered about the animals that are not already on the class table. (For example, "Does it have antennae?") Add these.

2. Then ask the class, "What do you think the pill bug needs to live?" Explain that students will observe the pill bugs in the terraria to discover what they eat and if they have what they need to live.

3. If you are not keeping the terraria on student desks, return the terraria to the storage area. Save the pill bug Venn diagram and **Record Sheet 9-A: Observing Woodland Animals** to use in Lesson 10.

**Extensions**

> SCIENCE

1. Have students find pictures of the pill bug's relatives (such as the shrimp, lobster, crab, and crayfish) and compare them with the pill bug. How are they alike and different?

> LANGUAGE ARTS

2. Read animal poems. Write a class poem about the pill bug. Or have groups or individual students write poems about their favorite animals.

> ART

3. Copy the outline of the pill bug on pg. 230 and try one of the ideas outlined in the **Extensions** in Lesson 7 (pgs. 94–95).

> SCIENCE   LANGUAGE ARTS

4. Help the class discover the names of some actual bugs and what makes them different from the pill bug. Share a book of poems that show the world from the bug's point of view, such as *When It Comes to Bugs*, by Aileen Fisher (see Bibliography).

**Assessment**

One way to monitor the sharpening of students' observation skills, is to examine new questions on the class observing table. Check for the following:

■ Did the class add questions that indicate the use of more than one sense?

■ Are the questions becoming more specific?

■ Are the questions focusing on more than one or two characteristics of animals? For example: Where is its mouth? Does it have legs?

**Note:** If you will be observing millipedes in Lesson 10, have your students bring in lettuce (or other green vegetables) and mushrooms to feed them.

**Record Sheet 9–A**

Name _____

Date _____

**Observing Woodland Animals**

**Pill Bug**

Observe it. Draw it.

**Bess Beetle or Millipede**

Observe it. Draw it.

The pill bug is _____

The Bess beetle or

millipede is _____

# Record Sheet 9–A *(continued)*

**Pill bug**

**Bess beetle or millipede**

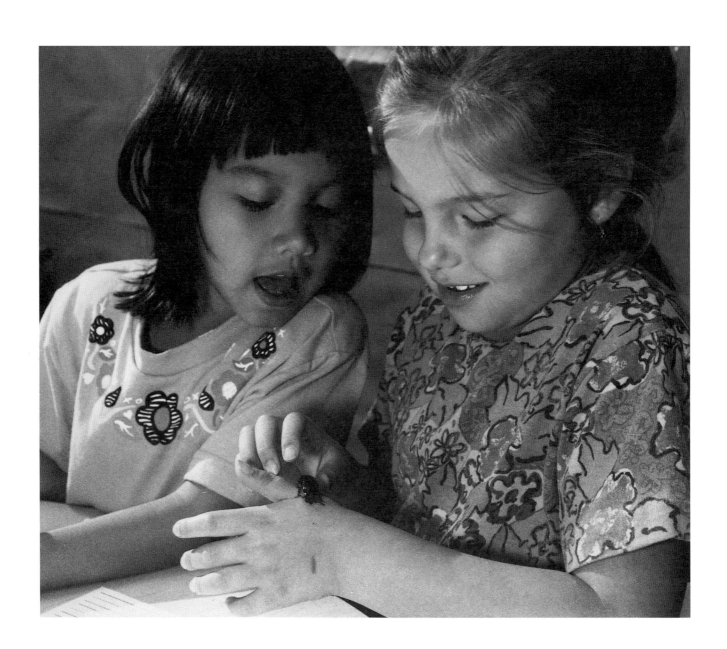

# Observing Bess Beetles or Millipedes: How Do They Compare with the Pill Bugs?

**Overview and Objectives**

Most children will probably have encountered a snail, guppy, and pill bug before this unit. In this lesson, students move from the familiar to the unfamiliar as they observe an animal with strikingly different physical characteristics. This experience helps further students' growing awareness of life's variety and their positive attitudes and sensitivity toward living things. In addition, it raises the idea that many organisms exist that students have never seen.

- Students observe, draw, and describe Bess beetles or millipedes.

- Students share their observations of the Bess beetle or millipede.

- Students use a Venn diagram to discuss the ways the pill bug and Bess beetle or millipede are similar and the ways they are different.

**Note:** For this lesson, you will receive either eight Bess beetles or eight millipedes. As you preview this lesson, please note that the procedure for Bess beetles differs from that for millipedes. Use only the **Background** and **Procedure** that apply to the animal your class is using.

**Background**

Scientists estimate that between 80 and 90 percent of all animal species on earth are insect species. And beetles alone include over 250,000 species—more than any other type of insect.

Beetles are found in all shapes, sizes, and colors. Like other insects, beetles have three distinct body parts, a pair of antennae, three pairs of legs, no bones, an exoskeleton, and special breathing holes along the sides of their abdomens. Like most adult insects, beetles have compound eyes.

Most beetles have two pairs of wings. The outer pair meet in a straight line down the middle of the back (a distinguishing characteristic of beetles). Typically tough and heavy, these wings function as shields that protect the insect's softer body and inner wings. The inner wings, which are thin and papery, are used for flying.

Although your students probably will not have the chance to witness it during this unit, beetles go through complete metamorphosis. They lay eggs that hatch as **larvae,** or **grubs.** The grubs of most beetles are white and have an enormous appetite.

Different types of beetle grubs eat different types of food. Grubs grow rapidly. As their bodies get bigger, the grubs molt at least three times. When the grubs have grown to full size, they become pupae in a protected place. Inside the shell of the pupa, the grub changes into an adult beetle. This change usually takes about a month. At that time, the adult beetle emerges from the pupa shell.

## Bess Beetles

This lesson brings one of the largest collectible beetles in the United States—the Bess beetle—into your classroom (see Figure 10-1). Known variously as the short-horned stag beetle, horn beetle, Peg beetle, patent leather beetle, and Bessbug, the Bess beetle is found in rotting logs from the eastern United States and Canada to Texas. Ranging in size from 32 to 36 cm (1¼ in to 1⅜ in), the Bess beetle has a long, black, shiny body, and hairy legs. While the Bess beetle has a second pair of wings, it almost never flies. On the occasions it does fly, its flight is short and clumsy.

*Figure 10-1*

*Bess beetle
(twice life size)*

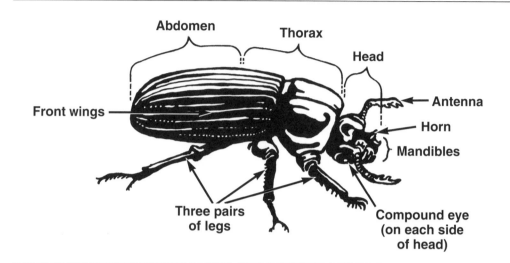

The Bess beetle's mouth is adapted for chewing wood. The beetle does not actually eat wood; instead, it chews through the wood with its hard mandibles to feed on the microorganisms that live inside. By breaking apart decaying wood, the Bess beetle hastens the decay process. Preferring to be with its food source and out of direct light, the beetle will seek the dark places in the terrarium, under wood or soil.

Though the male and female Bess beetle look almost identical, students who examine them closely can see that the male has a more prominent horn on his head. Students may also notice another interesting characteristic. These beetles communicate with each other by rubbing rough areas on the underside of their wings against a similar area on the top of their abdomens. This motion produces a squeaking sound that students may hear if the beetles are disturbed.

Although the Bess beetles have a formidable appearance, they are docile and harmless. If you and your students would like to, you can hold the beetles for a few minutes at a time. Some children will want to hold them immediately. Others may want to keep their distance (at least at first) until they grow comfortable with the beetles.

Bear in mind that if you show enthusiasm about these insects and encourage students to take their time, many will eventually grow comfortable enough to hold the beetles. On the other hand, some students may prefer simply to observe them in the cup and terrarium.

## Millipedes

**Millipedes** are one of the most ancient land animals on earth. They first appeared approximately 408 to 438 million years ago. Like pill bugs, they are arthropods. Roughly 80,000 species of millipedes are found throughout the world.

About 1,000 millipede species of varying sizes and shapes live in North America. The longest ones, about 16.5 cm (6½ in), are found in California. The millipede used in this unit is one of several species from a group called *Orthoporus*. In the United States, these millipedes live in woodland as well as desert environments in Texas, Arizona, and New Mexico. The adults are approximately 12.7 to 15.24 cm (5 to 6 in) in length. Because the millipedes are relatively large, it is easy for students to observe their different body parts (see Figure 10-2).

***Figure 10-2***

*Millipede*

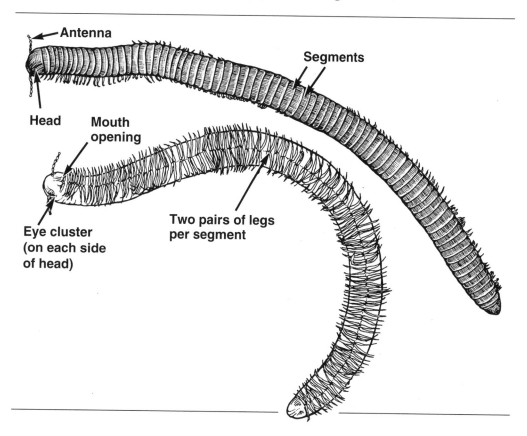

The millipede has a long segmented trunk and a round head with a pair of antennae. Two pairs of legs are attached to most body segments. It also has strong internal jaws, or **mandibles.** The entire body of most millipedes, including the one in this unit, is covered by a strong exoskeleton. Millipedes vary in color. Many are black or brown, but some are vividly colored.

Each of the millipede's body parts serves an important function. Its many legs— ranging from about 18 to over 750—help it push slowly forward by touching the ground in various stages of the backstroke. (The word millipede means "thousand-footed," but no millipede has that many feet.) As a millipede walks, it frequently taps the surface with its antennae, which have hairs for feeling and tiny projections scientists think may be used to smell and taste. Its strong jaws enable it to chew plant material. To burrow into the earth, the millipede lowers its head and pushes straight ahead.

Millipedes typically avoid light. Some are blind. Others, such as the millipede in this unit, have a cluster of simple eyes on each side of the head that are sensitive to light but do not actually see. The majority of millipedes live in dark, damp places: under stones, soil, or decaying material such as leaves, logs, and stumps. Millipedes benefit gardens by eating decaying plant material, which helps to recycle the minerals in soil.

Female millipedes lay their eggs in the soil. When they hatch, the young usually have only three pairs of legs. The number of segments and legs increases each time the millipede grows and molts. The millipede's growth pattern is called incomplete metamorphosis because there are only three life stages: egg, young (nymph), and adult. A complete metamorphosis usually contains seven immature stages. Millipedes may live for several years.

Millipedes are often confused with their close relatives, the centipedes. A key difference between the two animals is the number and arrangement of legs. Centipedes have only one pair of legs on each segment; millipedes have two pairs. Millipedes move more slowly than centipedes and do not bite or sting.

When disturbed, some millipedes "play dead." Longer ones coil up to protect their soft underside. Because they are slow-moving animals, most millipedes have developed another defense mechanism: a row of "stink glands" along each side of the body. These glands produce a bad-smelling substance that can deter predators. To humans, however, millipedes are quite harmless. Because the millipedes might release fluid from their stink glands when you are holding them, you and the students will wear plastic gloves during this lesson.

## Materials

*For each student*

1 **Record Sheet 9-A: Observing Woodland Animals** (from Lesson 9)
1 pencil
1 hand lens
1 pair of plastic gloves (for use with millipedes only)

*For each group*

1 plastic cup containing leaf litter and a Bess beetle or millipede, 2.66 ml (9 oz)
1 wood chunk (for use with Bess beetles only)
1 lid for plastic cup
1 sheet of newsprint (for use with millipedes only)

*For the class*

2 sheets of newsprint
1 holding tank with Bess beetles or millipedes
1 pill bug Venn diagram (from Lesson 9)
1 ladle
  Plant misters
  Markers
  Leaf litter
  Pieces of lettuce and mushrooms (for millipedes only)

## Preparation

1. Prepare a Bess beetle or millipede Venn diagram on newsprint.

2. When the Bess beetles or millipedes arrive, refer to Appendix A.

3. Just before the lesson, prepare one observing cup per team with a bit of leaf litter. Put one Bess beetle or millipede in each cup (see Figure 10-3). Use the ladle or a cup to gently scoop up one Bess beetle or millipede at a time. Be careful not to damage the legs or antennae. Wear plastic gloves when picking up the millipedes. Cover each cup with a lid.

*Figure 10-3*

*Putting the Bess beetle into an observing cup*

4. Before the lesson, spend a little time getting comfortable with the beetles or millipedes by examining both animals in observing cups. If you'd like, try holding one. Instructions for picking up each animal appear in Step 5 of the **Procedure.**

5. Label the second sheet of newsprint "What We Would Like to Find Out about Bess Beetles or Millipedes."

6. Arrange the class in the terrarium teams.

7. In Step 2 of the **Final Activities,** students discuss what the Bess Beetle or millipede needs to live. As with the pill bug, you will meet the Bess beetle's needs simply by maintaining the terrarium in general. If you have millipedes, feed them pieces of lettuce or other green vegetables and mushrooms.

**Procedure**

*If you are using the Bess beetle*

1. Explain that today the class will observe an organism that lives in the woods like the pill bug: a Bess beetle. Ask if students have ever seen a beetle. After they share experiences, explain that many of them may not have seen this particular kind of animal.

2. Now ask students to look at **Record Sheet 9-A: Observing Woodland Animals.** Explain that today they will observe, draw, and describe the Bess beetle. Write its name on the chalkboard and explain that each team gets two beetles.

3. Then ask, "What do you think an animal's mouth would look like if the animal chewed wood?" (Past students have said, "sharp," "pointy," "big.") Then distribute the observing cups.

4. Have the teams observe the beetle as they have done in previous lessons. After a minute or two, do the following:

   - Display the newsprint sheet labeled "What We Would like to Know about Bess Beetles."

   - Remind students they have talked a little about the beetle's mouth parts. Ask, "What would you like to find out about the Bess beetles?"

   - Write the questions on the newsprint.

   - Ask, "Which questions might we be able to answer by observing the beetle today?" Put a check next to these.

   - If the list does not contain a question about the legs, add "What do you notice about the beetle's legs?"

   - Show students the place on the record sheet where they can record observations.

   - Let students know that they can pick up the observing cup to observe the underside of the beetle.

5. At this point, help students who want to do so take the Bess beetle out of the observing cup. Refer to the instructions below.

   - To avoid damaging the legs and antennae, pick the beetle up by placing your fingers between the first and second pair of legs (see Figure 10-4). Do not try to pull a Bess beetle off yourself or another person. Let it crawl off.

   - Let the Bess beetle crawl out of the cup onto a desk or table or place it there yourself. Let it crawl around. You also can let it crawl from the surface onto your hand. Someone should be with a free beetle at all times to ensure its safety.

   - You can expect the beetle's hairy legs to tickle or even stick to your hand a bit. Also, the beetles may squeak since you are disturbing their routine.

*Figure 10-4*

*Picking up the Bess beetle*

■ Keep the Bess beetle out for no more than a few minutes at a time. When you are ready to return it to its observing cup or the terrarium, let it crawl in directly from your hand. Or pick it up from another surface and put it back inside the cup or terrarium.

6. Put each team's terrarium at its work area. Then give each team a wood chunk to place in the tank opposite from the plants. Have students gently tip the cups into the terraria and place the beetles on the side with the wood chunk. Have students moisten the wood chunks with the plant mister. Let them observe the beetles in the terraria.

7. Ask students to share Bess beetle observations. Record them on the right side of the Venn diagram you prepared earlier, and explain that this circle represents the beetles (see Figure 10-5). To get students started, ask questions such as the following:

■ What did you find out about the beetle?

■ What are some words that describe the beetle?

■ What is the beetle's body like?

■ What did you find out about its legs?

■ What did the beetle do while you were observing it?

***Figure 10-5***

*Bess beetle Venn diagram*

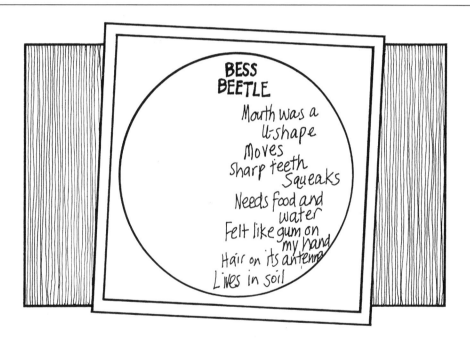

8. Now have students look again at their questions on the newsprint. Ask if they can answer any questions and circle those questions they have answered after making today's observations. Then add any new observations to the Venn diagram.

9. If some questions remain unanswered, let students know that they will be able to observe the beetles in the terrarium throughout the rest of the unit.

**Note:** It is important to keep the wood chunks moist so that the beetles can easily chew them. Also be sure to replace the wood chunks with fresh ones when they appear well chewed-up. See Appendix A for more information on maintaining the animals in the classroom.

*If you are using the millipede*

1. Explain that today the class will observe an organism that often lives in the woods like the pill bug: a millipede. Ask if students have ever seen a millipede. After they share experiences, explain that many of them may not have seen this particular animal.

2. Now ask students to look at **Record Sheet 9-A: Observing Woodland Animals.** Explain that today they will observe, draw, and describe the millipede. Write its name on the chalkboard and explain that each team gets one millipede.

3. Distribute the observing cups.

4. Have the teams observe the millipede as they have done in previous lessons. After a minute or two, do the following:

   ■ Display the newsprint labeled "What We Would Like to Know about Millipedes."

   ■ Ask, "What would you like to find out about the millipedes?"

   ■ Write the questions on the newsprint.

   ■ Ask, "Which questions might we be able to answer by observing the millipede today?" Put a check next to these questions.

   ■ If the list does not contain a question about the legs, add, "What do you notice about the millipede's legs?"

   ■ Show students the place on the record sheet where they can record observations.

   ■ Let students know they can pick up the observing cup to observe the underside of the millipede.

5. Millipedes will coil up in their cups. In order for students to observe the body parts and watch the millipede move, they will need to put it on newsprint. Offer students the following instructions:

   ■ Put on a pair of plastic gloves.

   ■ Remove the lid of the observing cup.

   ■ Place the millipede on the newsprint.

   ■ The millipede may try to crawl off the newsprint. As you observe it, gently nudge it back onto the newsprint.

   ■ To avoid startling the millipede, do not put your face close to it. Instead, lean in slightly to get a better look.

   ■ Keep the millipede out for no more than a few minutes at at a time. When you are finished observing the millipede, you or the teacher should gently put it back in the cup.

   ■ Before your team puts the millipede in the terraria, add more leaf litter.

   **Note:** At some point during the lesson or the next day, have students feed each millipede a mushroom or some lettuce while it is out on the newsprint. That way, students can observe the feeding closely. Keep a supply of fresh lettuce or mushrooms on hand for millipede food. Appendix A contains additional information on maintaining the millipedes in the classroom over time.

6. Put each team's terrarium at its work area. Have students gently tip the cups into the terraria and place the millipedes on the side opposite the seedling. Have students add pieces of lettuce or mushrooms to the terraria. Let them observe the millipedes in the terraria.

7. Ask students to share millipede observations. Record them on the right side of the Venn diagram you prepared earlier and explain that this circle represents the millipedes (see Figure 10-6). To get students started, ask questions such as the following:

   ■ What did you find out about the millipede?

   ■ What are some words that describe the millipede?

   ■ What is the millipede's body like?

   ■ What did you find out about its legs?

   ■ What did the millipede do while you were observing it?

*Figure 10-6*

*Millipede Venn diagram*

8. Now have students look again at their questions on the newsprint. Ask if they can answer any questions and circle those questions they have answered after making today's observations. Then add any new observations to the Venn diagram.

9. If some questions remain unanswered, let students know that they will be able to observe the millipedes in the terrarium throughout the rest of the unit.

**Management Tip:** If you choose to divide this lesson into two parts, this is a good stopping point.

**Final Activities**

1. Display the pill bug Venn diagram from Lesson 9 next to the Bess beetle or millipede Venn diagram. Explain that these circles contain students' observations of the pill bug and beetle (or millipede). You will use these circles to talk about how the two animals are alike and how they are different. Follow the instructions below on using the Venn diagrams to compare the pill bug and Bess beetle (or millipede).

   ■ As you did in Lesson 8, move the two diagrams together so that they overlap, creating an intersection. Use a marker to outline the center space.

   ■ Explain that in the center space, where the two circles overlap, you will use a different colored marker to list the ways the pill bug and Bess beetle (or millipede) are alike. To refresh students' memories, read aloud their pill bug observations.

   ■ Have the class look at the observations for both animals and indicate if any observations are true for both. As you write these observations in the center space, cross them out in the outer part of the circles. Remember, while the words may not match exactly, the concepts should be similar (see Figure 10-7).

**Figure 10-7**

*Comparing the pill bug and the Bess beetle*

   ■ To help students think of some other ways the pill bug and beetle (or millipede) are alike, ask, "What do both the pill bug and Bess beetle (or millipede) do?" "How do they act in their terrarium (habitat)?" Past students have added ideas such as the following: "They both eat," "They both need water," and "They both live on soil."

   ■ To highlight the ways in which the pill bug and Bess beetle (or millipede) differ, focus students on the observations that have not been crossed out.

2. Then ask the class, "What do you think the Bess beetle (or millipede) needs to live?" Explain that students will continue to observe and learn more about the Bess beetles (or millipedes) in the terraria.

3. Make sure the two circles are taped together so you can save the pill bug and Bess beetle (or millipede) Venn diagram for Lesson 14.

   **Note:** Refer to the Note on pg. 108 for ideas on encouraging students to observe the animals now that the freshwater habitats are set up. These ideas also apply to the woodland habitats. The Bess beetles and pill bugs usually will seek the moistest, darkest parts of the woodland habitat. Encourage students to find the animals and to discuss why they are not always visible. Students can dig the animals out and place them in sight. Then have students measure how much time it takes the animals to seek shelter.

**Extensions**

| LANGUAGE ARTS |

1. Read books such as *Keeping Minibeasts: Beetles*, by Bernie Watts (see Bibliography).

| LANGUAGE ARTS | | ART |

2. Have students write and draw about "the day I met the Bess beetle (or millipede)."

| LANGUAGE ARTS | | ART |

3. Read a book such as *Big Al*, by Andrew Clements (see Bibliography), to illustrate that what is different or ugly is not necessarily bad. Create a class display board illustrating the diversity of animal mouths or legs. Start by putting up a drawing of the Bess beetle's mouth or the millipede's legs. Ask students to add to the board.

| SCIENCE | | LANGUAGE ARTS |

4. Use mealworms (the larvae of the grain beetle) to observe the life cycle of a beetle. Mealworms are available in most pet stores. Put them in a plastic container with air holes. Give them some dry bran or oats and check on them daily to see if they are growing or need food. Eventually they will turn into pupae and then into adult beetles. Share a book about the change, such as, *Both Sides Now*, by Joni Mitchell (see Bibliography).

| LANGUAGE ARTS |

5. Explore insect movement with your class through song and dance. Try singing this to the tune of "Frère Jacques":

   *Crawling beetle, crawling beetle,*
   *On the ground, on the ground,*
   *Crawling, crawling, crawling,*
   *Crawling, crawling, crawling*
   *All around, all around.*

   Create other stanzas using the pill bug, guppy, and snail.

| LANGUAGE ARTS | | ART |

6. Copy the outline of the Bess beetle or millipede in Appendix C and try one of the ideas outlined in the **Extensions** section in Lesson 7 (pgs. 94–95).

**Assessment**

This lesson completes the group of lessons focused on the animals, in which students have produced several useful products for evaluation.

### Individual Student Products

**Record Sheet 7-A: Observing Freshwater Animals** and **Record Sheet 9-A: Observing Woodland Animals** offer information on how observing and recording skills have grown. As you review the sheets, keep these questions in mind:

- Have students' drawings become more detailed? What details are they now including?

- Have students recorded one or more observations?

- Have students' recorded observations become more descriptive? Which senses are students using to observe?

- Are students recording more than one characteristic of the organism?

You may want to pay especially close attention to the drawings of students who experience difficulty with writing or for whom English is a second language. If possible, meet with these students to give them the opportunity to talk about their drawings. Bear in mind that some students will be able to describe the organism in more detail verbally than in their drawing. Here are some points to consider:

- Does the student point to parts of the drawing as he or she discusses it?

- Does the student describe some of the organism's characteristics?

- Do the characteristics the student discusses appear in the drawing?

### Class Products

The Venn diagrams of the snail and guppy and of the pill bug and Bess beetle (or millipede) contain the outcome of four class discussions. Here are some points to consider as you review your discussions:

- Do the students' responses reflect their experiences?

- Are students able to compare the animals?

- Are students drawing on experience to make these comparisons?

- Did the class discuss a greater number of animal characteristics as the lessons progressed?

- Did the class identify some similarities between the snail and guppy and between the pill bug and Bess beetle or millipede (for example, basic needs and the ability to move)?

- Did students identify some of the animals' differences, such as specific needs (amount of moisture, type of food)?

### Teacher Observations

As you observe individual students, consider the following:

- Does the student visit the aquaria and terraria during the school day on his or her own?

- Is the student eager to share his or her observations?

- Does the student demonstrate care and sensitivity toward the organisms?

- Does the student talk about plants and animals other than those in the classroom, such as ones at home? Do students compare the other organisms with the plants and animals in the classroom?

# What's Happening in the Aquarium?

**Overview and Objectives**

Now that all of the organisms are in the aquaria and terraria, Lessons 11 and 12 provide scheduled time for the students to observe how the plants and animals may have changed. Earlier, students explored the concept that living things grow and change when they grew plants from seeds. This lesson reinforces that concept as it relates to the growth and change in the aquarium.

■ Students complete their pictorial record of the aquarium.

■ Students observe, discuss, and record any changes in the aquarium and its organisms.

■ Students write about one or more organisms in the aquarium.

**Background**

Depending on the conditions in your classroom and the aquaria, various changes will have occurred in the aquaria over the past few weeks. Changes in the plants are gradual and therefore more difficult to notice than changes in the animals. Whatever differences the students observe, they will discover that living things can grow, change, and experience birth and death. In general, you can expect some of the following changes to have occurred in the aquaria.

**Plants: *Elodea* and *Cabomba***

■ *Elodea* may have put out long, pale-green roots.

■ The *Cabomba* may have become dislodged and be floating.

■ Both plants may have grown longer or wider.

■ If available light was dim, one or both plants may have become less green and more brown.

■ One or both plants may have died.

■ Fish and snails may have eaten some of the plants.

**Animals: Snail and Guppies**

■ Snails may have laid eggs.

■ Snail eggs may have hatched.

■ Snails may have grown.

■ Snail shells may have changed color because of the level of minerals in the aquarium water.

■ The adult guppies may have grown.

■ The female guppy may have a swollen belly with black spots near the rear fin indicating pregnancy.

■ The female guppy may have had babies.

■ Some snails and guppies may have died.

**Aquaria**

■ The water may be cloudy.

■ Algae may be growing on the sides of the tanks.

■ Animal excrement may have accumulated in the gravel.

## Materials

*For each student*

1 **Record Sheet 5-B: Freshwater Picture** (from Lesson 5)
1 sheet of writing paper
1 pencil
1 hand lens

*For each group of students*

1 freshwater aquarium, 4 liters (1 gal)
1 pack of eight assorted crayons (optional)

*For the class*

Class questions about the snail (from Lesson 7)
Class questions about the guppies (from Lesson 8)
1 extra class aquarium (nursery tank), 4 liters (1 gal)
1 aquarium net, 5 cm (2 in)
1 ladle

## Preparation

1. Set out each team's freshwater aquarium and hand lenses.

2. If they are not still up, hang the class snail and guppy questions from Lessons 7 and 8.

3. Be sure every student has his or her **Record Sheet 5-B: Freshwater Picture** on hand.

   **Note:** If an organism has died and you would like to read students a book on death, refer to the Bibliography and Appendix B.

**Management Tip:** You may wish to do the **Final Activities** during language arts.

## Procedure

1. Explain to students that all the organisms they will study are now in the aquaria and terraria. Today, they will focus on the aquaria. Ask students what changes they might look for as they observe the aquarium organisms. List their thoughts on the chalkboard. Examples of past student responses include: "What are the animals doing?" "Did the plants grow?" "Are there any babies?"

2. Ask the class what organisms and how many of each were put in each aquarium. Write the names and numbers on the chalkboard as follows:

- One *Cabomba* and one *Elodea*

- Two snails and one male and one female guppy

3. Hold up one student's **Record Sheet 5-A: Freshwater Picture.** Explain that, as they observe, students should add the animals to the picture.

Students can also color in their drawings with crayons. Ask them **not** to color in the water, and to color lightly so that all parts of the aquarium are visible.

4. Give each student about 10 minutes to observe and complete the record sheets (see Figure 11-1). Circulate and listen to the groups as they work. Then discuss what they have seen in their aquaria. To draw out information, use questions such as the following:

- Has any organism changed? How?

- Are there more guppies or snails now than there were when you last looked? Are there more plants?

- Are any organisms missing? What do you think happened to them?

- Where does each animal like to be in the aquarium? What have you observed the animals doing in the aquarium?

- What do you think the snails eat? Why do you think so?

**Note:** Teachers have found it beneficial to keep a running list of changes students observe in the aquaria and terraria.

*Figure 11-1*

*Sample record sheet*

5. Give the children another 5 to 10 minutes to observe. Then repeat the above questions. Invite students to share an interesting observation they made some other time during the unit. Have students record one or two of these observations on the back of the record sheet.

6. Revisit the lists of snail and guppy questions from Lessons 7 and 8. Ask which questions students can now answer. Suggest that the class keep observing to try to find out more about the organisms.

   **Note:** According to your class's skill level, you may want to do the **Final Activities** as a class, in small groups, or individually.

## Final Activities

1. Now that students have observed, discussed, and cared for the organisms in the aquaria, ask them to write or dictate individual stories about their aquaria. (Some students have written both fiction and nonfiction.) Let students draw as well as write (see Figure 11-2). Students have written about some of the following topics:

   - The life of the snails, guppies, or plants

   - The aquarium home

   - Birth and death in the aquarium

   - How the organisms live together

   - What it would be like to live in the aquarium (from the viewpoint of a fish or snail)

2. Distribute the writing and drawing paper.

3. Invite students to share their work.

## Extensions

**ART**

1. Have students make stick puppets to accompany their writings. Share their work with the class.

**ART**

2. Have students use large black construction paper and pastel chalks to create pastels or dioramas of the aquaria.

**SCIENCE**    **ART**

3. Make an edible aquarium with your class. Tell students you will be using gelatin and gummy fish and brainstorm what other foods you might use to represent the other elements of an aquarium. Make blueberry gelatin by adding one and one-quarter cups of cold water with ice cubes to a package of powdered mixture. Stir until thickened and add the gummy fish and other foods. Refrigerate for one hour. Then let the class eat its aquarium.

**LANGUAGE ARTS**

4. Working with students in small groups, share the wordless book *In the Pond,* by Ermano Cristini and Luigi Puricelli (see Bibliography). Ask each student or team of students to write a story to accompany the pictures.

**Figure 11-2**

*Sample student writing*

Emily McCleary

Raymond Silva

**LANGUAGE ARTS**     **ART**

5. Copy the journal sheet on pg. 65 for each student. Have students draw and write about their thoughts throughout the day.

**MATHEMATICS**

6. Using the theme of freshwater plants and animals, set up a math learning center with activities that invite students to develop number sense and to practice addition combinations.

**Assessment**

In Lessons 11 and 12, students discuss how things have changed in their aquaria and terraria. Consider some of the following questions:

■ How closely are the students observing?

■ How well are students able to verbalize what they observe?

■ Do the students make any connections between the plants and animals? For example, "The snails eat the plants."

■ Do students have more questions after observing and discussing the aquarium or terrarium?

■ Are students becoming more aware that organisms grow and change over time?

In addition, students revisit their lists of animal questions from earlier lessons. If students have questions they still cannot answer, discuss how they might find out the answers, such as by going to the library or asking animal experts at zoos, nature centers, or museums.

The writings of young children may reveal what has impressed them the most from their recent experiences as well as things they have learned. Remember that writing ability is a limiting factor. Provide time for those students who need it, to talk with you about pictures they have drawn or to elaborate on their writing. Students also can use stick puppets to dramatize their observations of the aquarium organisms. Teachers have also found it helpful to create a language experience story about the freshwater animals and plants, much like the seed story created in Lesson 6.

# What's Happening in the Terrarium?

**Overview and Objectives**

Following the same process as in Lesson 11, students now focus on growth and change in the terrarium. This broadens the class's understanding of growth and change in organisms and enables students to apply their growing observing and recording skills.

- Students complete their pictorial record of the terrarium.

- Students discuss and record any changes in the terrarium and its organisms.

- Students write about one or more organisms in the terrarium.

**Background**

Depending on the conditions in your classroom and the terraria, various changes will have occurred in the terraria over the past few weeks. Changes in the plants and animals in the terraria are gradual and more difficult to pinpoint than changes in the aquaria. For example, the pill bug, Bess beetle, and millipede do not reproduce as often as guppies do, and the process is less easy to observe. In general, you can expect some of the following changes to have occurred in the terraria.

### Plants: Tree Seedling and Moss

- The seedling may have grown in height and grown more needles.

- The seedling may have lost needles, turned brown, or died.

- The seedling may have been dislodged by the animals.

- The moss may have developed spore stalks.

- The moss may have died.

- The moss mat may have been broken apart by the animals.

### Animals: Bess Beetles, Millipedes, and Pill Bugs

- If pill bugs are in different stages of molting, they will range in color from brown to gray to black. They also will range in size.

- There may be baby pill bugs.

- Some of the Bess beetles or millipedes and pill bugs may have died.

- The Bess beetles or millipedes may have dug tunnels.

**Terraria**

- Water may be condensing on the sides.

- The animals may have dug holes.

- The leaf litter may have been eaten.

- The wood chunks may have been chewed.

**Observing the Terrarium Organisms**

In contrast to the aquarium animals, the terrarium ones are not always visible. The pill bugs tend to stay in or near the moss or under the twigs and leaves. Remind students to be patient. Even if the pill bugs do not emerge right away, eventually they will show themselves. The Bess beetles usually will stay under the wood chunk. If students observe the wood moving, they can locate the beetles. The millipedes usually burrow into the soil or under the leaf litter.

To locate the animals today, students may need to use a pencil or stick to poke around gently. It is important, however, that they do not dislodge the pine tree or the moss. Let students know that it is fine to lift the wood chunk to observe the beetles.

**Materials**

*For each student*

   1  **Record Sheet 4-B: Woodland Picture** (from Lesson 4)
   1  sheet of writing paper
   1  pencil
   1  hand lens

*For each group*

   1  pack of crayons (optional)
   1  woodland terrarium, 6 liters (1½ gal)

*For the class*

     Class questions about the pill bugs (from Lesson 9)
     Class questions about the beetles or millipedes (from Lesson 10)

**Preparation**

1. Set out each team's terrarium and hand lenses.

2. Be sure every student has **Record Sheet 4-B: Woodland Picture.**

3. If necessary, hang the lists of beetle or millipede and pill bug questions from Lessons 9 and 10.

**Procedure**

1. Let students know that today they will observe the terrarium closely. Ask what they might look for as they observe the terrarium organisms. List their thoughts on the chalkboard.

2. Ask the class what organisms and how many of each were put in each terrarium. Write the names and numbers on the chalkboard as follows:

- One tree seedling and one moss mat

- Two pill bugs and one Bess beetle or millipede

Now hold up one student's woodland picture record sheet (see Figure 12-1) and explain that, as they did for the aquarium, they will observe the terrarium and add the animals to the picture.

**Note:** Students can color in their woodland pictures. Ask them not to color too darkly. All parts of the terrarium should be visible.

*Figure 12-1*

*Sample record sheet*

Record Sheet 4–B

Name Tristan Date March 8 199

**Woodland Picture**

STC / Organisms

**Tristan Benjamin**

3.  Share with students that the terrarium animals may be harder to locate than the aquarium animals, and ask students why they think this is so. Then ask the class if they have observed where the animals like to be in the terrarium. Show students how to carefully uncover the beetles or millipedes and pill bugs.

4.  Give students about ten minutes to observe and complete the woodland picture. Discuss with them what they have seen in the terrarium. To draw out information, use questions such as the following:

    ■  Has any organism, plant, or animal changed? How?

    ■  Are there more of beetles, millipedes, or pill bugs now than when you last looked? Is there more moss? Are there more seedlings?

    ■  Are any organisms missing? What do you think happened to them?

    ■  Have any other parts of the terrarium changed? (For example, wood chunks may be chewed.)

    ■  What do you think the pill bugs and Bess beetles or millipedes are eating? How do you know?

    ■  Where in the terrarium did you find the pill bugs and beetles or millipedes? What have you observed the animals doing in the terrarium?

5. Give the children another 5 to 10 minutes to observe, and then repeat the above questions. Invite students to share an interesting observation they have made any other time during the unit. Have students record one or two of these on the back of their woodland pictures.

6. Revisit the lists of pill bug and Bess beetle or millipede questions from Lessons 9 and 10. Ask which questions students can answer now. Suggest that the class keep observing to try to find out more about the organisms.

**Final Activities**

1. Now that children have observed, discussed, and cared for the terrarium and its organisms, ask them to write or dictate individual stories about them (see Figure 12-2). Some students have written about the following topics:

   - The life of the pill bugs, Bess beetles or millipedes, or plants

   - The terrarium home

   - Birth and death in the terrarium

   - How the organisms live together

   - What it would be like to live in the terrarium from the viewpoint of a pill bug, Bess beetle, or millipede

2. Distribute the writing and drawing paper.

**Figure 12-2**

*Sample student writing*

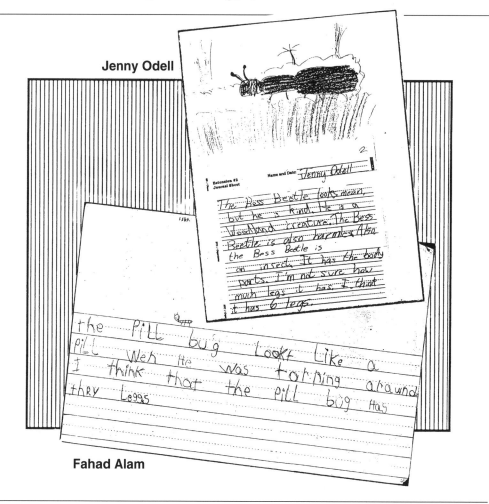

Jenny Odell

Fahad Alam

**Extensions**

> **ART**

1. Have students make stick puppets to accompany their writings. Then have them share their work with the class.

> **MATHEMATICS**

2. Make the logic problems on pgs. 146–147 into overheads to do as a class. (Students may also work individually or in small groups.) For the plant problem, as you read and discuss a clue, decide as a class which plant is being described and place a check in that box. Repeat this procedure for the animal problem. Develop other logic problems or ask students to create one for another day.

> **LANGUAGE ARTS**   **ART**

3. Read books about life in a forest, such as *How the Forest Grew*, by William Jaspersohn (see Bibliography) and have the class create a diorama of a forest. Or if you have made a woodland mural, have students add other organisms to it.

> **LANGUAGE ARTS**   **ART**

4. Work with students in small groups and share a wordless book such as *In the Woods*, by Ermano Cristini and Luigi Puricelli (see Bibliography). Ask each student or a team of students to write a story to accompany the pictures.

> **SCIENCE**

5. To broaden children's experiences, take the class outside the classroom to explore the variety of organisms in other environments. Appendix D outlines some outdoor activities.

   **Note:** Teachers have found it beneficial to create a language experience story about the woodland animals and plants, much like the story about the seeds created in Lesson 6.

**Logic Problem**

Name

Date

| Carlos | Moss | Tree Seedling |
|---|---|---|
| Amy | | |

Carlos's plant is not very small, and it has a stem.

Amy's plant does not have roots.

# Logic Problem

| | Bess Beetle or Millipede | Pond Snail |
|---|---|---|
| Chin | | |
| Shana | | |

Chin's animal has a head but does not have six legs.

Shana's animal has a head but does not live in water.

# Freshwater and Woodland Plants: How Do They Compare?

## Overview and Objectives

Now that students have observed, discussed, and cared for all the organisms over time, they are developing an understanding that organisms grow, change, and have general and specific needs. In this lesson, students focus their discussion on just the plants in the unit. In what ways are the plants alike? In what ways are the plants different? What do plants need to live? Such questions lay the groundwork for the next few lessons, in which—moving from the specific to the general—students begin to form their own ideas about the ways plants and animals are alike and different.

- Students observe the freshwater and woodland plants.

- Students use a Venn diagram to discuss ways the freshwater and woodland plants are alike and different.

- Students add to their "Needs of Plants" list.

- Students learn more about the variety among plants by reading about some unusual ones.

## Background

In this lesson, students focus on all four plants they have observed—*Elodea*, *Cabomba*, tree seedling, and moss—to arrive at ways plants are alike and different. Following is a sampling of past student responses.

**Ways the Plants are Alike**

- They are mostly green and brown.

- They grow.

- They need air, water, and light.

- They are living.

- They need a place to live.

- They can die.

**Ways the Plants are Different**

- Size.

- Shape (structure).

- Some live in water, some on land.

By this time, most students will recognize that plants need water, air, light, and a place to live. At this age, however, students may not grasp that nutrients from the soil are dissolved in the water and absorbed by the plants or that plants make their own food. As discussed previously, it is natural that young students view water simply as the plants' food. In addition, students may not yet understand that plants, like animals, reproduce.

## Materials

*For each student*
1   pencil
1   hand lens
1   copy of the reading selection "Four Amazing Plants" (blackline master on pgs. 155–159)

*For each group*
1   freshwater aquarium, 4 liters (1 gal)
1   woodland terrarium, 6 liters (1½ gal)
2 or 3   Post-it™ notes, 102 × 152 mm, (4 × 6 in), or strips of paper, 28 × 8 cm (11 × 3 in)

*For the class*
2   sheets of newsprint
3   markers of different colors
"Ways the Woodland Plants Are Alike" list (from Lesson 4)
"Ways the Freshwater Plants Are Alike" list (from Lesson 5)
"Needs of Plants" list (from Lesson 6)
1   roll of transparent tape

## Preparation

1.  Prepare the plant Venn diagram according to the following directions.

    ■  Draw a large circle on one sheet of newsprint and label it "Woodland Plants."

    ■  Copy the "Ways the Woodland Plants Are Alike" list onto the left side of the circle (see Figure 13-1).

    ■  Use a different colored marker to draw a second circle. Copy the "Ways Freshwater Plants Are Alike" list onto the right side of the circle.

    ■  Tape the two circles together. Outline the intersection of the two circles (see Figure 13-2).

    ■  Hang the large Venn diagram where you and the class can easily add to it.

**Management Tip:** Read Steps 3 through 5 of the **Procedure** to decide whether you want to use Post-it™ notes.

2.  If you are not using Post-it™ notes, cut two or three idea strips out of writing paper for each team.

3.  Make a copy of the reading selection "Four Amazing Plants" (pgs. 155–159) for each student. Read the story and judge whether you will want to read it with the students as a class or with them in small groups. You may also want them to have a chance to read it again with a partner before beginning Step 1 of the **Final Activities.** This reading selection is not in the Student Notebook.

**Figure 13-1**

Copy the list onto the left side of the circle.

**Figure 13-2**

Outline the intersection of the two circles.

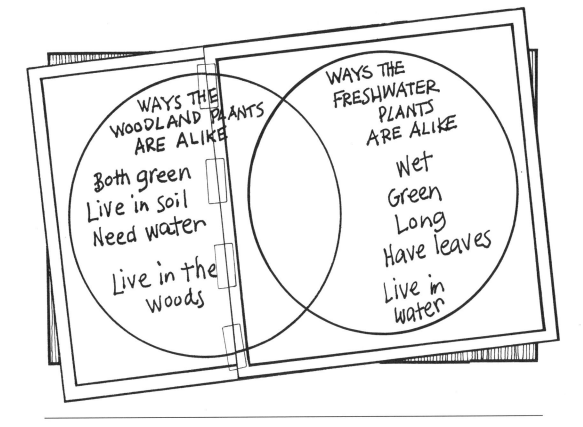

Freshwater and Woodland Plants: How Do They Compare? / **151**

4. Arrange the class in the terrarium and aquarium teams or, if you prefer, create new groups of four. Pick a student who writes fairly well to act as a recorder for each group.

**Management Tip:** You may choose to do the **Final Activities** during language arts.

**Procedure**

1. Give each group a terrarium, aquarium, and hand lenses. Also give two or three idea strips or Post-it™ notes to each group's recorder. Explain that today the class will talk about all four of the plants in their tanks.

2. Focus students on the Venn diagram and describe how they will use the circles to compare the freshwater and woodland plants. Then point out that the lists on the two diagrams are students' own observations from earlier lessons. Read both lists to the class.

3. Now ask each group to observe the freshwater plants in their tanks. If a group discovers a new likeness not already in the freshwater plant circle, ask the recorder to write it on an idea strip or Post-it™ note. Ask groups to repeat this process for the woodland plants.

4. Have groups share their ideas with the class and then attach them to the circles.

5. Now ask the class to look at the whole Venn diagram.

   ■ Try questions such as the following:

      ▪ How are all the plants alike?

      ▪ What are some observations that appear in both circles?

      ▪ What is true about the plants in both tanks?

   ■ Using a different-colored marker, write the ways the plants are alike in the center space and cross out corresponding statements in the outer parts of the circles. Or record them on Post-it™ notes. You will transfer these characteristics to a new Venn diagram in Lesson 15.

6. Then focus on the observations in the outer part of the circles that are not crossed out. Ask the class, "What are some of the differences between the plants?"

7. Now ask, "How are the plants you grew from seeds like the freshwater and woodland plants? How are they different?"

8. Display the sheet labeled "Needs Of Plants." Remind students that they wrote this list after caring for plants they grew from seeds. Since then, they have cared for plants in the terraria and aquaria. Ask the following questions:

   ■ What do you think these plants need to live and be healthy?

   ■ What should we add to our list? Why?

   ■ What did we do to care for our plants so they could live?

9. Then ask what the classroom plants, plants on the playground, and plants in students' homes all need to live. Add any new thoughts to the "Needs of Plants" list.

10. Finally, ask if some plants have needs that others do not. (For example, *Elodea* needs to live in water; moss does not.)

   **Note:** Save the plant Venn diagram and the class "Needs of Plants" list to use in Lesson 15. If display space is a problem, you can now take down the class observing table and the lists of specific animal questions.

**Final Activities**

1. Distribute the reading selection "Four Amazing Plants." Explain that, as students have discovered, there are many kinds of plants. This selection will tell them about some plants they may never have heard of before. As students read, give them time to draw themselves in each plant picture. After the reading, have students add a picture to the cover page and combine the pages into a book. Students can take the book home to share with their families.

2. After the reading, refer to the **Extensions** for some follow-up activities.

**Extensions**

SCIENCE    SOCIAL STUDIES

1. After the reading, have your class try some of the following activities:

   ■ Have students share experiences they have had with interesting plants. Where did they see the plants? Why were they interesting?

   ■ On a map, locate the places the four plants can be found. Then find out about interesting plants in your community.

   ■ Visit a botanical garden or nursery that has a wide diversity of plant life. Many have plants such as Venus flytraps, common water lilies, and cacti.

LANGUAGE ARTS    ART

2. Discuss some of the many ways plants are helpful to us. Good books to start with are *From Wood to Paper* and *From Tree to Table,* by Ali Mitgutsch, and *Corn Is Maize,* by Aliki (see Bibliography). Then:

   ■ Create a board to illustrate the ways plants are helpful or make a "Plants Are Helpful" wheel (see Figure 13-3).

   ■ Have students create a graph of their families' favorite fruits. Give students a copy of the take-home activity on pg. 160 and go over this sheet with them. Later, create a class graph of the students' results.

*Figure 13-3*

*"Plants Are Helpful" wheel*

**LANGUAGE ARTS**

3. We are not the only animals that depend on plants for many things. Try one of these books to begin a discussion (see Bibliography):

   ■ *The Gift of the Tree,* by Alvin Tresselt

   ■ *The Cactus Hotel,* by Brenda Z. Guiberson (features a saguaro cactus)

**SCIENCE**

4. To further emphasize plant variety, bring in a cactus, begonia, coleus, or other plant, for the class to observe and compare with the plants they have studied.

**SOCIAL STUDIES**

5. Have students share ethnic dishes their families make using plants. Create a class map of foods illustrating the cultural diversity in your class. In addition you can plan a "whole-plant" class lunch featuring plants such as lettuce, broccoli, and cabbage.

**MATHEMATICS**

6. Using the theme of terrarium plants and animals, set up a math learning center with activities that invite students to develop number sense or to practice addition combinations.

# Four Amazing Plants

Amazing plants grow in different parts
of the world. Now we will find out about
four of these amazing plants.

## The *Rafflesia* (rah-*flee*-zee-uh):
A plant with the largest flower in the world

Borneo is the name of an island in the Pacific Ocean.
A giant flower lives in the jungles there.
It is the *Rafflesia,* or monster flower.
The flower can grow to be 1 to 1⅓ m, or 3 to 4 feet, wide.
It is a beautiful pinkish-red color with orange markings.
The flower is the only part of the plant
that lives above the ground.
The rest of the plant lives underground.

**Put yourself in the picture:** Draw yourself
smelling the monster flower. But hold your nose!
It smells very bad.

## The Giant Water Lily:
The largest water plant in the world

The giant water lily lives in still waters
of the Amazon River in South America.
This plant's roots and most of its stem
are under water. But the leaves and flowers
of the giant water lily float on top of the water.
Its floating leaves can be big enough for you
to lie on. But not strong enough to hold you.

## Put yourself in the picture:
Lie on the giant water lily leaf.

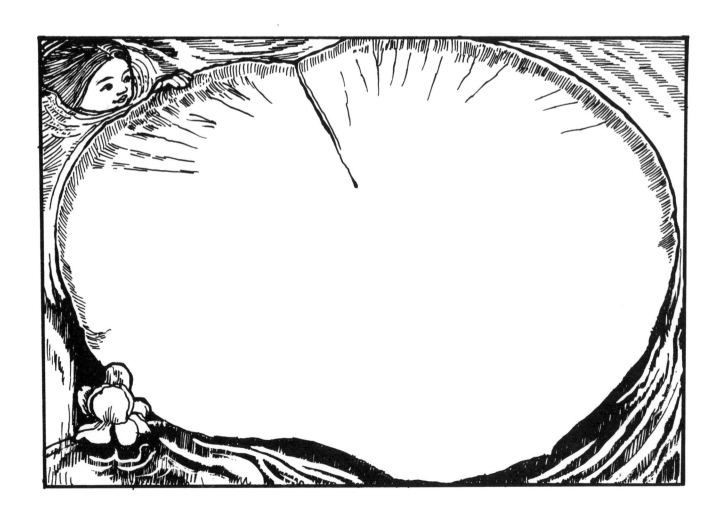

## The Saguaro (sah-*gwah*-row) Cactus:
The largest cactus in the world

A tall green plant grows in the
deserts of Arizona, California, and Mexico.
This plant is called the saguaro cactus.
It can grow to be 50 feet (about 15 m) tall.
That makes it the largest cactus in the world.
It does not rain much in the desert. When it does rain,
this is what the cactus does: its body stretches
to hold extra water.

## Put yourself in the picture:
Draw yourself next to the big saguaro cactus.
Where will the top of your head be?

## The Venus Flytrap:
A plant that eats animals

A plant that eats flies? Yes, it is true.
The Venus flytrap lives in North Carolina
and South Carolina. It has leaves that snap shut
to trap insects inside. This is how it happens.
Each leaf of the Venus flytrap has six hairs on it.
When a fly lands on a leaf
and touches a hair once, nothing happens.
But what if the fly touches a hair twice?
Or two hairs at the same time? SNAP, the leaves shut!
The fly is trapped.

## Put yourself in the picture:
Feed the Venus flytrap. It eats mostly insects.

**My Family's
Favorite Fruit**

Name _____

Date _____

Everyone eats fruit, and fruit is part of a plant.
What is your family's favorite fruit to eat?
Find out and color in a box for each person's favorite fruit.

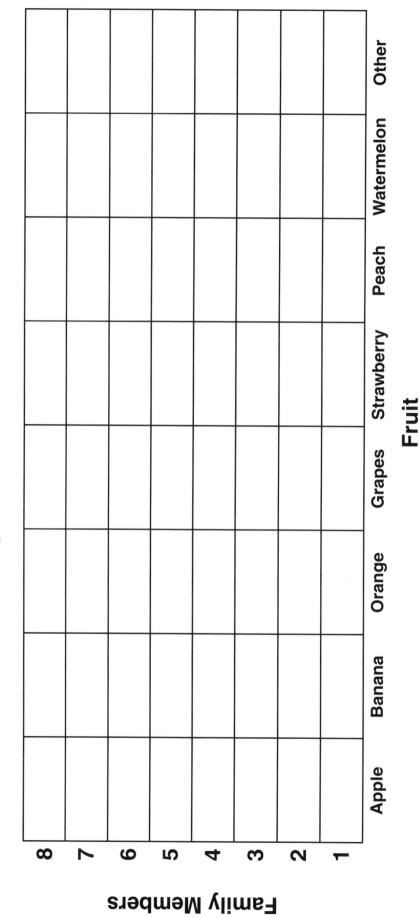

**Family Members**

8
7
6
5
4
3
2
1

Apple    Banana    Orange    Grapes    Strawberry    Peach    Watermelon    Other

**Fruit**

Circle the fruit your family likes most.

# Freshwater and Woodland Animals: How Do They Compare?

**Overview and Objectives**

Having discussed the ways the plants are alike and different, students are ready to switch the focus back to animals. By continuing a class dialogue about the ways organisms are alike and different and what they need to live, students become more aware that there are characteristics common to all animals as well as characteristics specific to different kinds of animals. In addition, by investigating the different ways animals move, children have the opportunity to apply their emerging graphing and classifying skills.

- Students observe the freshwater and woodland animals.

- Students use a Venn diagram to discuss ways the freshwater and woodland animals are alike and different.

- Students generate a "Needs of Animals" list.

- The class makes a graph of the different ways animals move.

**Background**

In this lesson, the students focus on all four animals they have observed—pond snail, guppy, pill bug and Bess beetle or millipede—to arrive at ways these animals are alike and different. Following is a sampling of past student responses.

**Ways the animals are alike**

- They grow.

- They need air, water, and food.

- They have babies.

- They are living.

- They need a place to live.

- They move.

- They eat.

- They can die.

**Ways the animals are different**

- Size.

- Shape.

- Color.

- The way they move.

- Some live in water; some on land.

- Some make a sound.

- Their bodies have different parts, such as wings and antennae.

- They eat different kinds of food.

Students also will consider what animals need to live and be healthy. As mentioned earlier, most animals need food, water, air, a place to live, and some type of shelter.

In this lesson's **Final Activities,** the class creates a graph illustrating the different ways animals move. In the past, many children tended to choose some of the same animals, such as rabbits, squirrels, and snakes. One way to increase animal variety is to combine the activity with a visit to the school library, where students can find out about many kinds of animals.

**Management Tip:** You may choose to do the **Final Activities** during math.

## Materials

*For each student*
   1   pencil
   1   hand lens

*For each group*
   1   freshwater aquarium, 4 liters (1 gal)
   1   woodland terrarium, 6 liters (1½ gal)
2 or 3   Post-it™ notes, 102 × 152 mm, (4 × 6 in), or strips of paper, 28 × 8 cm (11 × 3 in)

*For the class*
   3   sheets of newsprint, 61 × 90.4 cm (24 × 36 in)
   3   markers of different colors
      Snail and guppy Venn diagram (from Lesson 8)
      Pill bug and Bess beetle Venn diagram (from Lesson 10)
   1   roll of transparent tape
   1   Post-it™ notepad, 102 × 152 mm (4 × 6 in)
   1   large sheet of butcher paper for class graph

## Preparation

1. Prepare the animal Venn diagram according to the following directions.

- Draw a large circle on one sheet of newsprint and label it "Freshwater Animals."

- Onto the left side of this circle, copy the list of snail and guppy similarities (the intersection) from the Venn diagram from Lesson 8 (see Figure 14-1).

- Use a different colored marker to draw a second circle. This time, copy the list of pill bug and Bess beetle or millipede similarities from the Venn diagram from Lesson 10 onto the right side of the circle.

- Tape the two circles together. Outline the intersection of the two circles (see Figure 14-1).

- Hang this Venn diagram where you and the class can easily add to it.

**Figure 14-1**

*Sample Venn diagram*

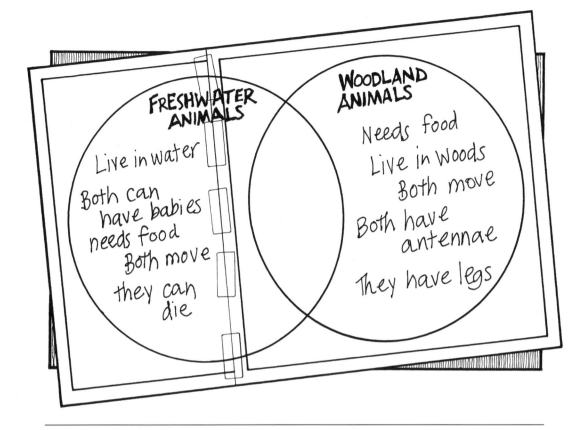

FRESHWATER ANIMALS

Live in water

Both can have babies
needs food
Both move
they can die

WOODLAND ANIMALS

Needs food
Live in woods
Both move
Both have antennae
They have legs

2. Label the third sheet of newsprint "What We Think Animals Need."

3. Label the butcher paper "Ways Animals Move."

**Management Tip:** Read Steps 3 to 5 of the **Procedure** to decide whether you want to use Post-it™ notes.

4. If you are not using Post-it™ notes, cut two or three idea strips out of writing paper for each team.

5. Arrange the class in the terrarium and aquarium teams or if you prefer, create new groups of four. Pick a student recorder for each group.

**Procedure**

1. Give each group a terrarium, aquarium, and hand lenses. Also give two or three idea strips or Post-it™ notes to the group recorder. Explain that today the class will talk about all four of the animals in their tanks.

2. Focus students on the Venn diagram representing the two kinds of animals. Explain that they will use the circles to compare the freshwater and woodland animals. Then point out that the Venn diagrams describing these animals are students' own observations from earlier lessons. Read both Venn diagram lists to the class.

3. Now ask each group to observe the freshwater animals in their tanks. If a group discovers a new likeness—not already in the freshwater animal circle—ask the recorder to write it on an idea strip or a Post-it™ note. Ask groups to repeat this process for the woodland animals.

4. Have groups share their ideas with the class and then put them up on the circles.

5. Now have the class look at the whole Venn diagram. Do the following:

   ■ Try questions such as

      ▪ How are all the animals alike?

      ▪ What are some observations that are in both circles?

      ▪ What is true about all the animals?

   ■ Using a different-colored marker, write the ways the animals are alike in the center space and cross out the corresponding statements in the outer part of the circles. Or, record them on Post-it™ notes. These characteristics will be transferred in Lesson 15 to a new Venn diagram.

6. Then focus on the observations in the outer part of the circles that are not crossed out. Ask the class, "What are some differences between the animals?"

7. Display the sheet labeled "Needs of Animals." Remind students that they have cared for the animals in the terraria and aquaria and have discussed ways the animals are alike and different. Then ask the following questions:

   ■ What do you think the animals need to live and be healthy?

   ■ What did you do to care for the animals so they could live?

8. Then ask students what the animals on the playground and pets in their homes need to live. How do they care for their pets? Add any thoughts that are not on the list of what animals need.

9. Ask if some animals have different needs that other animals do not (for example, the Bess beetle needs to live around wood; the pond snail does not.)

   **Note:** Save the animal Venn diagram and the class "Needs of Animals" list to use in Lesson 15.

## Final Activities

1. Discuss with students that, as they have discovered, one way animals are like each other is that they move. One way they are different from each other is the **way** they move. Then display the sheet labeled "Ways Animals Move."

2. Starting with the aquarium, ask students, "How does the guppy move?" Have a student record their answer in drawings or words on a Post-it™ note and place it under the "swim" column (see Figure 14-2).

3. Repeat Step 2 for the snail, pill bug, and Bess beetle or millipede.

4. Give each student a Post-it™ note. Ask students to draw an interesting animal and write its name on the drawing. (If time permits, have students look through books to find different animals. Otherwise, ask them to draw an animal that other students may not know about.)

5. Have each student add his or her drawing to the graph. Add new categories as the need arises.

## Extensions

MATHEMATICS

1. Take a class trip to the zoo or natural science center. Then have students add to the "Ways Animals Move" graph.

**Figure 14-2**

"Ways Animals
Move" graph

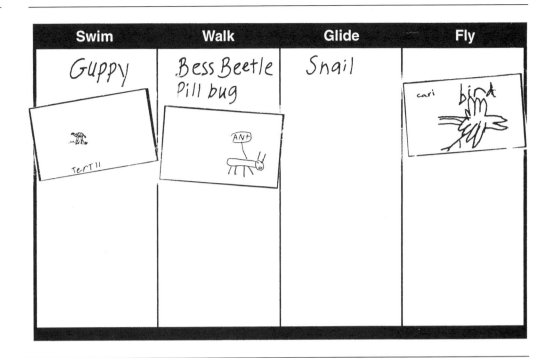

| Swim | Walk | Glide | Fly |
|------|------|-------|-----|
| Guppy | Bess Beetle Pill bug | Snail | |

---

2. Read a book such as *The Salamander Room,* by Anne Mazer (see Bibliography) that tells about what you need to consider when you bring an animal from the wild into your home to live. Keep a list of the ways the main character, Brian, changes his room for the salamander. Then ask students what they think the salamander needs to live. Why does Brian's bed end up in the woods at the conclusion of the story?

3. Read a book such as *City Critters around the World,* by Amy Goldman Koss (see Bibliography) that illustrates the variety of animals that live in different places. Then have students draw animals that live in their town or city. Try this in different seasons to discover which animals are seen only in certain seasons and which are observable year-round. Also have students whose families have lived in different countries or regions share information on animals that live in these places.

4. Discuss with the class what makes an animal a good pet. Why don't many people have pet bears? Why are hamsters a popular pet? Have students decide on the best class pet and adopt one for the class.

5. Discuss some ways in which animals are helpful to people and some ways in which we are helpful to animals. Have each student create a "Helpful Animals" wheel.

# How Are Our Plants and Animals Alike and Different?

**Overview and Objectives**

Students have now explored how their plants are alike and different and how their animals are alike and different. They have also discovered what their plants and animals need to live. While students have observed both kinds of organisms in the same environment, they have not yet focused specifically on comparing the plants with the animals. In this lesson, students make that comparison as they think about all the plants and animals they have observed and how they are alike and different.

- Students discuss the ways in which all the organisms they have observed are alike and different.

- Students use a Venn diagram to discuss the similarities and differences between the freshwater and woodland plants and animals.

- Students generate a list of the needs of plants and animals.

- Students read about how a zookeeper meets the needs of a crocodile.

**Background**

In this culminating lesson, students generate ideas about how all the organisms they have studied are alike and different. Your class's lists are likely to include some of the following ideas that other students have expressed.

**Ways plants and animals are alike**

- They are living.
- They need food, air, and water.
- They can die.
- They need a place to live.
- They can grow.

**Ways plants and animals are different**

- Animals move from place to place.
- Most plants need light to live.
- They need different food.
- They look different. Animals have eyes and a mouth.

Most students will not mention "having babies" as a similarity between plants and animals. The concept of the seed as the "baby" of a plant is still somewhat abstract for students of this age to grasp. Because they have grown plants from seeds and, possibly, have read books about seeds, your students may make this connection now or in later grades.

**Materials**

*For each student*
1 pencil
1 hand lens
1 pair of scissors
1 **Cutout Page** (blackline master on pg. 179)

*For each group*
1 **Comparing Plants and Animals** (blackline master on pg. 180)
1 freshwater aquarium, 4 liters (1 gal)
1 woodland terrarium, 6 liters (1½ gal)
2 or 3 Post-it™ notes, 102 × 152 mm, (4 × 6 in), or strips of paper, 28 × 8 cm (11 × 3 in)
Glue

*For the class*
3 sheets of newsprint
2 markers (two different colors)
Plant Venn diagram (from Lesson 13)
"Needs of Plants" list (from Lesson 13)
"Needs of Animals" list (from Lesson 14)
Animal Venn diagram (from Lesson 14)
Transparent tape

**Preparation**

1. Prepare the plant and animal Venn diagram according to the following directions.

   ■ Draw a large circle on one sheet of newsprint and label it "Plants."

   ■ In the left side of this circle, copy the list of plant similarities (the intersection) from Lesson 13's Venn diagram. If you used Post-it™ notes, move these to the new circle.

   ■ Using Lesson 14's list of animal similarities, repeat the above steps using a different colored marker and putting the list on the right side of the circle.

   ■ Tape the two circles together, overlapping them. Outline the intersection and hang the new Venn diagram (see Figure 15-1).

2. Make one copy of the blackline master **Comparing Plants and Animals** (pg. 180). Copy onto it the two lists from the class Venn diagram you have just made. Then make one copy of the sheet for each group of four to six students.

3. Make one copy of the blackline master **Cutout Page** (pg. 179) for each student.

4. Examine the reading level of "A Crocodile Comes to the Zoo" on pgs. 175–178 and decide if you want students to read it as a class or in small groups. You may also want students to have a chance to read it again with a partner.

**Figure 15-1**

Sample Venn diagram

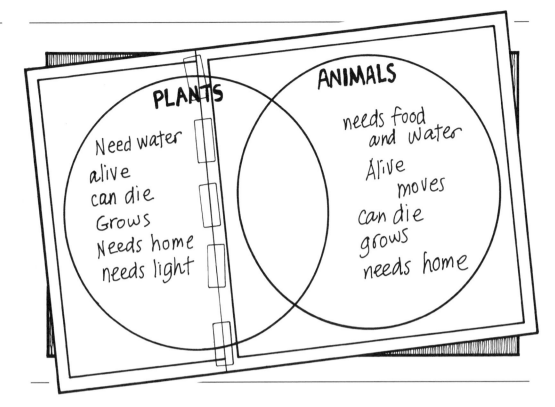

5. Label the third newsprint sheet "What We Think Plants and Animals Need" and hang it. Have on hand or display the two lists from Lessons 13 and 14, "Needs of Plants" and "Needs of Animals."

6. Arrange the class in groups of four to six and choose a recorder for each.

**Procedure**

1. Share with students that today they will talk about all the plants and animals they have observed in the unit.

2. Focus students on the Venn diagram you have just made. Explain that today they will compare the plants and animals. Point out that the lists describing the plants and animals are their own lists from the last two lessons. Then have students read the lists aloud.

3. Distribute a copy of **Comparing Plants and Animals** to each group. Point out that it is just like the class Venn diagram. Ask students to share ideas about how they can use it to list the ways the plants and animals are alike. To help students complete their sheets, use questions such as the following:

   ■ How do you decide the ways in which the plants and animals are alike?

   ■ How do you decide which ideas in each list describe both plants and animals?

   ■ Where do you write the ways in which the plants and animals are the same?

   ■ What words do you put a line through?

4. When you think the class grasps how to fill in the Venn diagram, have each group work together on the sheet (or, if you prefer, work on the activity as a whole class). Ask the recorder to write in what the group members want to put in the center space of the two circles. Distribute the terraria and aquaria and encourage the groups to observe and refer to them as they work. Figure 15-2 shows an example of past student work.

**Figure 15-2**

*Sample student
work*

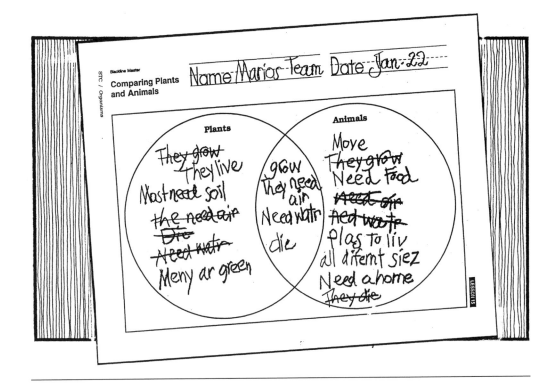

Blackline Master
STC / Organisms
**Comparing Plants
and Animals**

Name Marias Team Date Jan 22

Plants

Animals

They grow
~~They grow~~ They live

Mostneed soil

~~the need air~~

~~Die~~

~~Need water~~

Meny ar green

96w
They need air
Need watr
die

Move
~~They grow~~
Need Food
~~Need air~~
~~ned water~~
Plas to liv
al difernt siez
Need a home
~~They die~~

LESSON 15

**Final Activities**

1. When all groups have one or two similarities on the **Comparing Plants and Animals** sheet, focus students on the class Venn diagram. Follow these steps:

   ■ Have a group share one way in which the plants and animals are alike.

   ■ Have a group member come up to cross out a likeness in the two lists and add it to the center space on a Post-it™ note. If a new similarity is suggested, add it to the Venn diagram.

   ■ Repeat these steps with another group.

2. Read aloud the class list of the ways plants and animals are alike. Then focus on the observations that are in the outer part of the circles and are not crossed out. Ask the class, "What are some ways the plants and animals are different?"

3. Display the class "Needs of Animals" and "Needs of Plants" lists from Lessons 13 and 14. Also display the sheet labeled "Needs of Plants and Animals." Have the class look at both lists. Then ask these questions:

   ■ What do both plants and animals need to live and be healthy?

   ■ What needs are on both the plant list and the animal list?

   Record responses on the new sheet. Leave this list, as well as the class plant and animal Venn diagram, on display.

4. Collect the **Comparing Plants and Animals** sheet from each group.

5. Later in the school day, or during language arts, read "A New Crocodile Comes to the Zoo" on pgs. 175–178.

   ■ Before you begin, ask students what they think a zookeeper should put in a crocodile home so it can live.

   ■ Write down their ideas.

- Then read "A New Crocodile Comes to the Zoo" with the class. Have students cut and paste the drawings from the cutout page onto the crocodile's new home as they read.

- After the reading, ask students such questions as:

  - Did their list contain some of the things Mike put into the crocodile's home?

  - What needs does the crocodile have that are like some of the needs of other animals they have studied?

  - What needs does the crocodile have that are special or different from those of other animals they have studied?

6. Choose some of the following applications to enhance the reading selection:

   - If you choose to adopt a class pet (see Extension 4, pg. 174) read about the animal with the class. Have students design a home that will meet the animal's needs. Enlist the help of the school librarian.

   - Suppose a new monkey was coming to the zoo. Ask children which of its needs are just like the crocodile's. Does the monkey have any other special needs? Have the class go to the library to find out.

   - Read a book such as *Working Frog*, by Nancy Winslow Parker (see Bibliography), the story of a frog who comes to live in a reptile house at a zoo and has a crocodile for a neighbor. Discuss the ways in which the frog's zoo home is similar to that of the crocodile. Also discuss the frog's specific needs.

**Extensions**

LANGUAGE ARTS

1. To emphasize that organisms are found everywhere, read a book such as *The Vacant Lot*, by Dale Fife, about a "vacant" lot that is actually a home to many organisms (see Bibliography).

LANGUAGE ARTS

2. To introduce the concept of nonliving, have the class list all the living things in the terrarium or aquarium. Then have them list what is left. What would they call this second list?

LANGUAGE ARTS

3. Write a language experience story with the class about the plants and animals they cared for during the unit. The following questions may help facilitate the writing.

   - Before we could keep living things in the classroom, we had to get ready for them. What did we do to get ready for the freshwater and woodland organisms?

   - What organisms did we keep in each home?

   - How did we care for the organisms?

   - After we observed the organisms for a few weeks, how did they change? Did anything new appear?

   - What did we find out about what plants and animals need to live?

Ideas for using the class story include the following:

- Make individual books for each student from their experience stories and have students illustrate them. Students can read the books with you or on their own.

- Have each student draw one picture to illustrate part of the class story and make a class book.

- Have your students share their story with another class or with their parents.

  [ LANGUAGE ARTS ]

4. Take students to the library and challenge them to find out the differences between alligators and crocodiles. Have them write about and illustrate their findings.

  [ SCIENCE ]    [ ART ]

5. Visit a zoo with your class and have each student pick one animal on which to focus. Have students draw the animal's zoo home. Then back in the classroom, have each student share his or her drawing and explain how the zoo meets the animal's needs. In addition, invite a zookeeper into your classroom and have him or her talk about how the zoo meets the needs of its animals and plants.

## Assessment

In Lessons 13 through 15, students have used Venn diagrams to compare plants to plants, animals to animals and, finally, plants to animals. The **Assessment** section in Lesson 10 (pg. 130) presented some guidelines to help you review the class and small group Venn diagrams. Here are some additional points to consider:

- Are the students progressing in their ability to use a Venn diagram for comparison?

- Can the students identify some likenesses between groups of organisms? For example: basic needs, tendency to grow, change, and die.

- Can students identify some differences between groups of organisms? For example: appearance, structure, special needs, where the organism lives.

- Do students' comments reflect their experiences in the unit? For example, "Plants and animals need water because we had to give some to all of them when we took care of them."

- Are students able to list some basic needs common to plants and animals?

- Do students understand that organisms not only have needs in common with other organisms but also have specific needs?

- Is there evidence that students have become more aware of the diversity of life?

- Are students able to identify some of the basic needs of a crocodile?

- Are students able to compare the crocodile's needs with those of the animals they have been studying?

**Reading Selection**

## A Crocodile Comes to the Zoo

Welcome to the zoo. I'm Mike, the zookeeper.

It's a big day at the zoo.
A crocodile is coming here to live.
And we want him to feel at home.

How big should his home be?

Big enough to move around in.

Most living things need air, water, food,
and a place to live.

So first, I will give the crocodile water.
Crocodiles need water to drink and swim in.
**Color in the water on the big picture.**

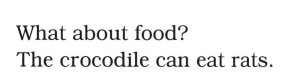

What about food?
The crocodile can eat rats.

So when he is hungry, I'll give him rats to eat.
**Cut out the rat on your cutout page.**
**Then glue it onto the big picture of the**
**crocodile's new home.**

But every kind of animal has special needs, too.

The crocodile needs to keep warm. So his home
will have big windows to let in the sun.

**Cut out the sun and glue it onto the picture.**

**176**

Crocodiles need a place to hide and to make a nest for eggs. Plants and land will work just fine.

**Cut out the plants on your cutout page. Then glue them on the X's in the big picture of the crocodile's new home.**

Then color in the plants. And color the land, too.

That's what the crocodile needs to live and be healthy.

**So cut him out and put him into his new home.
You can also color in the rest of the picture.**

# Cutout Page

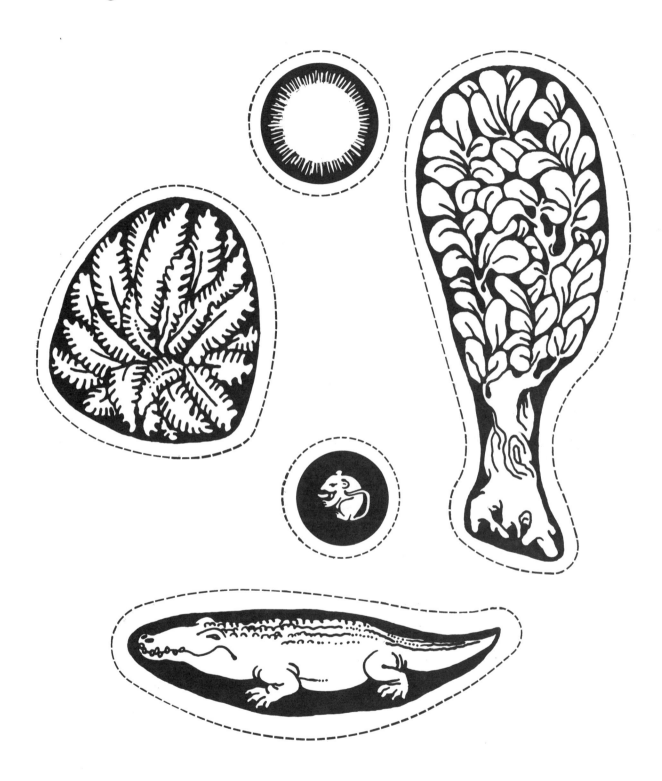

**Comparing Plants
and Animals**

Name

Date

Animals

Plants

# Taking a Look at Ourselves

**Overview and Objectives**

Students have now discussed and compared all the plants and animals in the classroom except one animal—themselves. Now they are ready to apply what they have learned about these living things to humans. By comparing themselves with the living things they have observed, students explore their own relationship to other living things. How are we like them? How are we different? Through this comparison, students are introduced to the concept that humans are organisms and have similar needs to those of other organisms.

- Students observe and describe humans.

- Students compare humans to other animals and plants.

- Through words and drawings, students express ways in which they think humans are like other animals and like plants.

**Background**

This may be many students' first experience thinking about themselves as similar to other animals and plants—or about themselves as being animals. Most students, however, will cite one or more similarities and differences. And, some students may even point out that the key difference between humans and most other species lies in our verbal and intellectual abilities. Listed below are examples of some students' responses.

**Ways People Are Similar to Plants and Animals**

- We are living.

- We need food, water, air, and living space.

- We grow.

- We need a place to live.

- We can die.

**Ways People Are Different from Plants and Animals**

- We look different (body structure, for example).

- We wear clothes.

- We talk.

- We are very intelligent.

The fact that we are animals may be a difficult concept for some children. In the **Final Activities,** you will ask students how they think we are like other animals and like plants. After completing this unit, many students will realize that we are, indeed, animals. By providing experiences that help students clarify their ideas about living things and humans, this lesson helps students make this realization when they are ready.

**Materials**

*For each student*

 1 pencil
 1 sheet of white drawing paper, 30 × 46 cm (12 × 18 in)
 1 hand lens

*For each group of four*

 1 marker
 1 sheet of newsprint
 1 **Ways Animals and Plants Are Alike** (blackline master on pg. 189)
 1 **Comparing Humans with Other Animals and Plants** (blackline master on pg. 190)
 1 roll of transparent tape
 1 Post-it™ notepad, 38 × 50 mm (1½ × 2 in)
   Scissors

*For the class*

   Class plant/animal Venn diagram (from Lesson 15)
   Class "Needs of Plants and Animals" list (from Lesson 15)
   Crayons or markers

**Preparation**

1. Display the class plant/animal Venn diagram and the class "Needs of Plants and Animals" list from Lesson 15.

2. Copy the list of ways animals and plants are alike from the Venn diagram and the "Needs of Animals And Plants" list from Lesson 15, onto the blackline master **Ways Animals and Plants Are Alike** (pg. 189) Be sure to record each similarity in its own box. Depending on your class, you may need to use more than one copy of the blackline master. Make one copy of the completed blackline master for each group of four students.

3. Make one copy of the blackline master **Comparing Humans with Other Animals and Plants** (pg. 190) for each group of four students.

4. Have a pair of scissors and a roll of tape on hand for each group of four students.

5. Prepare each group's sheet of newsprint by drawing a line lengthwise to divide the sheet in half. Then label one column "Alike" and the other column "Different." Title the sheet "Humans."

6. Arrange the class in groups of four.

   **Note:** Teachers have found it beneficial to place students with classmates they have not worked with before. This gives teachers a different perspective from which to assess student growth. For example, students may more readily share ideas in different groups.

**Procedure**

1. Remind students that over the past several weeks they have discussed how plants and animals are alike and different. Today they will discuss one more organism in the classroom: humans.

2. Invite groups to observe each other carefully. Let them know they can use a hand lens if they like, just as they did with the other organisms in this unit.

3. After several minutes, ask the class to share one way they think humans are alike. Hand out the prepared newsprint, marker, and Post-it™ notepad to each group. Choose a recorder for each group and help him or her record the class's idea on a small Post-it™ note and place it in the "alike" column on their newsprint. Repeat this for a way humans are different from each other.

4. Next, explain that you would like each group to think of more ways humans are alike and different and record them on their newsprint the same way. Encourage groups to extend their thinking beyond how humans look to things all humans do or need. (For example, "Humans eat." "Humans need air.")

5. After a few minutes, ask the groups to share their ideas. Let groups know they can add to their lists if a different group has an idea with which they agree.

6. Ask students if they think there may be ways humans are like other animals and plants. Then let students know that they have learned enough in this unit to find these ways out on their own. Give each group the scissors, tape, a copy of **Ways Animals and Plants Are Alike,** and a copy of **Comparing Humans with Other Animals and Plants.**

7. Select a student in each group to cut out each of the ways plants and animals are alike from the Ways Animals and Plants are Alike sheet. Let students know these are their ideas from Lesson 15. Then have a different student tape these items onto the left circle on the Venn diagram on the Comparing Humans with Other Animals and Plants sheet.

8. Have a student in each group move the Post-it™ notes from the "Alike" column on their newsprint sheet to the right circle on the Venn diagram. Ask the groups to use this Venn diagram to discover ways humans are similar to plants and other animals just like they did in Lesson 15.

9. When students have finished, have each group show the class their Venn diagram and share ways they discovered humans are like other organisms.

10. Using the group's Venn diagrams, discuss with the class the ways in which humans are different from plants and other animals.

**Final Activities**

1. Give each student a piece of drawing paper. Then write these two sentence starters on the chalkboard:

   ■ I am like other animals because _____.

   ■ I am like a plant because _____.

   Read the sentence starters to the class. Tell students to copy one of the sentence starters onto the top of their drawing paper and fill in the blank with (or dictate to an adult) one or more reasons (see Figure 16-1). Then invite students to illustrate their writing.

2. Collect the group's Venn diagrams, drawings, and writings.

*Figure 16-1*

*Sample student writing*

**Tyler Carroll**

I am like other animals because I eat meet and I need a home and I need water, I am ~~like plant because~~ We both grow. slep

I am more like a plant because i nead air that is clean, water, home, i am tall like a stik.

**Shana Gooden**

## Extensions

**ART**  **SCIENCE**

1. Have students make a "My Needs Wheel" illustrating what they think they need to live and be healthy, including any special needs they may have.

**ART**  **LANGUAGE ARTS**  **SOCIAL STUDIES**

2. Illustrate the diversity in people by sharing a book such as *People*, by Peter Spier (see Bibliography). Then illustrate the diversity in the class by graphing characteristics such as eye color, ethnic background, or hair color. Or have students trace around the outside of each other's bodies to create paper people. Have students fill in features in the cutouts. Also investigate the diversity in humans around the world in terms of food, clothing, and types of homes.

LANGUAGE ARTS    SCIENCE

3. Read a book such as *A House Is a House for Me,* by Mary Ann Hoberman (see Bibliography). Have the students draw their own homes. Investigate other animal homes with the class and create a display.

SCIENCE    ART

4. Just as the students drew the growth of their plants, have students illustrate their own development from birth to their present age. Invite students to add what they think they will look like as a teenager, adult, and older adult. Then have students compare human growth and change to the life cycle of the snail or the beetle or to the life cycle of the plants students grew from seeds.

LANGUAGE ARTS    SCIENCE

5. For a follow-up activity, share an adaptation of the classic circular rhyme, "The Tree in the Wood," by Christopher Manson (see Bibliography). The song encompasses an entire cycle of change and rebirth.

MATHEMATICS

6. Investigate the diversity in humans by having students explore "people row patterns."

   ■ Choose a characteristic such as hair color.

   ■ Have each student draw a picture showing a person with a specific hair color.

   ■ Spread out all the pictures face down on the floor, and have a student turn over three of the pictures. (This gives you a pattern—for example, brown, brown, blonde.)

   ■ Ask three students who represent this pattern to come to the front of the room. Then have other students extend the pattern.

   ■ Ask students to describe the pattern in other ways, such as with letters—for example, brown, brown, blonde can be described as a, a, b. Or, have students snap and clap to represent this pattern—for example, snap, snap, clap.

**Assessment**

When evaluating the class discussions, group products, student drawings, and writings, here are some questions to focus your thoughts:

   ■ How well were students able to apply their experiences in the unit to humans?

   ■ Do students show growth in their ability to make comparisons among different organisms?

   ■ Were students able to use their Venn diagrams to discover some ways in which humans are similar to other animals and to plants?

   ■ What differences did students cite between humans and other animals and plants?

   ■ Did students provide plausible reasons why humans are like other animals or plants?

After completing this unit, you may want to consider the following questions:

- Are students asking more questions?

- Are students sharing ideas more readily with each other?

- Do students follow directions and routines more independently?

- Are students using a wider variety of ways to express themselves?

- Are students showing more sensitivity toward living things?

- Are students talking about living things other than those in the unit?

*Post-Unit Assessment*

The post-unit assessment (pgs. 193–195) is a matched follow-up to the pre-unit assessment in Lesson 1. Comparing students' pre- and post-unit responses to the same set of questions allows you to document their learning.

*Additional Assessments*

Additional assessments for this unit are on pgs. 197–199.

# Ways Animals and
# Plants Are Alike

**Comparing Humans
with Other Animals
and Plants**

Name

Date

**Humans**

**Plants and Animals**

# Post-Unit Assessment

**Overview**

This post-unit assessment is matched to the pre-unit assessment of students' ideas about living things. By comparing the individual and class responses from these two activities with those from Lesson 1, you will be able to document and assess students' learning over the course of the unit. During the first lesson, students individually drew a living thing and wrote about the things they thought it needed to live and be healthy. They also developed two class lists entitled "Ways We Think Plants and Animals are Alike" and "Ways We Think Plants and Animals are Different."

When they revisit these activities during the post-unit assessment, students are likely to appreciate how much they have learned about the needs of living things, as well as about the ways plants and animals are alike and different.

**Materials**

*For each student*
- 1 pencil
- 1 **Record Sheet 1-A: My Living Thing**

*For the class*
- 2 sheets of newsprint
  Class lists from Lesson 1: "Ways We Think Plants and Animals Are Alike" and "Ways We Think Plants and Animals Are Different"
- 2 markers

**Preparation**

Label one sheet of newsprint "Ways We Think Plants And Animals Are Alike" and label the other "Ways We Think Plants And Animals Are Different." Date the sheets and post them in the classroom.

**Individual Drawings**

**Procedure**

1. Remind students that in the unit's first lesson they drew a living thing and what they thought it needed to live and be healthy. Explain that you would like them to do this again to find out if their ideas have changed.

   **Note:** Make sure students cannot see their drawings from Lesson 1 as they complete Step 2.

*Sample student drawings*

**Lauren Jones**

2. Distribute the record sheets. Ask students to do the following:

- Put their names and today's date on the paper.

- Draw a living thing in the middle of the paper.

- Add to the drawing what they think the living thing needs to live and be healthy.

- Label the parts of the drawing.

- Complete the sentences at the bottom of the drawing. (As in Lesson 1, you may need to have some students discuss their drawings with you.)

3. When reviewing the drawings, you may find the following guidelines helpful:

- Do the second drawings depict a living thing? Did more students draw plants the second time?

- Do the drawings represent student growth? Does the second drawing include more of the basic needs of living things (food, water, air, shelter or a place to live)? Any specific needs? (For example, a polar bear needs a colder climate.)

- Did the students go a step further and include other living things or show relationships between living things?

- Have students grown in their ability to communicate ideas through writing, drawing, and discussion?

4. Have the class generate a new list of living things. Compare this list to the one from Lesson 1.

- Does the new list contain only living things?

- Does the new list contain a wider variety of living things? Are there more plants on the list?


## Class Lists

1. Remind students that by now they have observed and discussed a variety of living things. You would like them again to share ways they think plants and animals are alike and different.

2. Focus the class on the ways living things are alike, first by asking, "In what ways are plants like animals, or animals like plants?" Have the class share ideas. Record all responses. Repeat this for the list of differences.

3. Now display the original lists from Lesson 1. Here are some ways to use the lists to assess student progress:

- Ask students to point out statements on the original lists that they now know, without a doubt, to be true. What experiences did they have during the unit that confirmed these statements? Questions such as "How do you know that?" and statements such as "Tell what happened next" may be helpful.

- Ask students to correct or improve statements and give reasons for their corrections.

- Ask students to point out information on their new lists that is not on the original ones.

4. Ask students which activities in the unit they liked best. Have them explain why.

5. Continue adding to the class lists throughout the school year.

# Additional Assessments

**Overview**

Following are some suggestions for assessment activities. It is not essential to do all these activities. Select those you think will be helpful in evaluating your students' learning.

■ Assessment 1 provides you with sample questions to use when conducting student meetings. You can use this activity to assess every student or to assess only those who express themselves better verbally than they do in written form.

■ Assessment 2 is a collection of student work: record sheets, student writing, and journal sheets.

■ Assessment 3 encourages students to share their experiences in this unit with visitors.

## Assessment 1: Student Meetings

**Materials**

*For each student or pair of students*
    1   terrarium or aquarium

*For you*
    1   pencil
1 or 2  sheets of paper

**Procedure**

1. Meet with a student or a pair of students and examine a terrarium or aquarium.

2. Record students' responses to questions such as the following:

   ■ What can you tell me about the aquarium (or terrarium)?

   ■ What does this (point to an animal or a plant) need to live and be healthy?

   ■ Pick two living things in the terrarium (or aquarium). What are some ways they are like each other? What are some ways they are different from each other?

   ■ In what ways are you like this (point to an animal or plant)? In what ways are you different?

3. As you review students' responses, think about whether students have an understanding of the following:

- The basic needs of living things

- The ways living things are similar and different

- That humans are living things who are both similar to and different from other living things

## Assessment 2: The Collection of Student Work

**Materials**

*For each student*
Collection of individual work products

**Procedure**

1. Keep all students' products at school until the end of the unit.

2. Review each student's individual work. As you evaluate the products, consider the following criteria:

- How complete are the products?

- Do the products indicate effort on the student's part?

- Which specific activities or concepts were hard for the student to do or grasp?

- Do the products reflect the student's growth?

- Can students express themselves through drawing, writing, and speaking?

- Have their observations become more descriptive?

3. Meet individually with students whose written work you would like to discuss.

4. For those students who had difficulty observing and describing the organisms, consider one of the following ideas:

- Set up a learning center that includes the class observing table. Add a variety of interesting objects for students to observe and describe.

- Take the students outside to observe and describe different plants and animals.

- Conduct observing and describing games in small groups or with the whole class.

- Have a student describe a "mystery object" in the room. Let the other students try to figure out what it is.

- Create an observation scavenger hunt in the classroom, in the school, or outdoors. Create descriptions of the objects each team is to collect.

## Assessment 3: Students Share Their Work with Visitors

**Materials**

*For the class*

> Aquaria and terraria
> Variety of class lists, Venn diagrams, and individual student work

*For you*

1 pencil

1 notepad of paper

**Note:** Students often reveal a great deal about what they have learned from the *Organisms* unit when they are given the opportunity to talk with visitors.

**Procedure**

1. Invite visitors , such as the principal, other teachers, parents, or another class to your classroom.

2. Listen and take notes as students talk with the visitors about the living things in the terrarium or aquarium. Encourage students to show their work products as they discuss the unit. To help students share their experiences, try questions such as the following:

   ■ What did you do to learn how plants grow? What did you learn?

   ■ Describe the freshwater home you set up. What living things did you place in this home? What can you tell us about them?

   ■ Describe the woodland home you set up. What living things did you place in this home? What can you tell us about them?

   ■ What did you have to do to make sure all the living things were able to live in the classroom and be healthy?

   ■ What were your favorite living things you observed? Why?

   ■ What surprised you? What interested you the most?

   ■ In what ways are the woodland animals similar to each other? In what ways are they different? (Repeat this line of questioning for the woodland plants, freshwater animals, and freshwater plants.)

   ■ In what ways are you like the other animals you observed? In what ways are you different? (Repeat this with the plants.)

   ■ What do you need to live and be healthy?

   ■ In what ways are most living things similar? Different?

# Bibliography: Resources for Teachers and Students

The Bibliography is divided into the following categories:

- Resources for Teachers
- Resources for the Class

Resources for the Class is subdivided into the following categories:

- Observing
- Habitats
- Seeds and Plants
- Animals
- Death
- Films and Videocassettes
- Computer Software

While not a complete list of the many books written on organisms, this bibliography is a sampling of books that complement this unit. These materials come well recommended. They have been favorably reviewed, and teachers have found them useful.

If a book goes out of print or if you seek additional titles, you may wish to consult the following resources.

*Appraisal: Science Books for Young People* (The Children's Science Book Review Committee, Boston).

Published quarterly, this periodical reviews new science books available for young people. Each book is reviewed by a librarian and by a scientist. The Children's Science Book Review Committee is sponsored by the Science Education Department of Boston University's School of Education and the New England Roundtable of Children's Librarians.

National Science Resources Center. *Resources for Teaching Elementary School Science*. Washington, DC: National Academy Press, 1996.

This volume provides a wealth of information about resources for hands-on science programs. It discusses science curriculum materials, supplementary materials (science activity books, books on teaching science, reference books, and magazines), museum programs, and elementary science projects.

*Science and Children* (National Science Teachers Association, Washington, DC).

> Each March, this monthly periodical provides an annotated bibliography of outstanding children's science trade books primarily for pre-kindergarten through eighth-grade science teachers.

*Science Books & Films* (American Association for the Advancement of Science, Washington, DC).

> Published nine times a year, this periodical offers critical reviews of a wide range of new science materials, from books to audiovisual materials to electronic resources. The reviews are primarily written by scientists and science educators. *Science Books & Films* is useful for librarians, media specialists, curriculum supervisors, science teachers, and others responsible for recommending and purchasing scientific materials.

*Scientific American* (Scientific American, Inc., New York).

> Each December, Philip and Phylis Morrison compile and review a selection of outstanding new science books for children.

Sosa, Maria, and Shirley M. Malcom, eds. *Science Books & Films' Best Books for Children, 1988–91.* Washington, DC: American Association for the Advancement of Science Press, 1992.

> This volume, part of a continuing series, is a compilation of the most highly rated science books that have been reviewed recently in the periodical *Science Books & Films.*

## Resources for Teachers

Bowden, Marcia. *Nature for the Very Young.* New York: John Wiley, 1994.

> Good resource for inventive activities for each season.

Brown, Vinson. *How to Make a Miniature Zoo.* New York: Dodd, Mead, 1987.

> The third edition of a classic guide to animal care, from creating a terrarium to creating a schoolyard that attracts wildlife.

Bruchac, Joseph. *Native American Animal Stories.* Golden, CO: Fulcrum, 1992.

> A wonderful collection of stories to read aloud, this is the companion to *The Keepers of the Animals,* also by Joseph Bruchac.

Caras, Roger. *A Zoo in Your Room.* New York: Harcourt Brace Jovanovich, 1975.

> A guide to keeping small creatures in the classroom, emphasizing the preservation of wildlife and respect for animals' needs.

Connell, Joseph. *Sharing Nature with Children.* Nevada City, CA: Dawn Publications, 1979.

> A good resource for nature activities to share with young children.

Criswell, Susie Gwen. *Nature with Art.* New York: Prentice Hall, 1986.

> An extensive source of classroom and outdoor activities linking art and natural history. The projects are divided into four categories: plants, animals, people, and places.

Damrosch, Barbara. *The Garden Primer.* New York: Workman, 1988.

> A general reference book on gardening.

Dishon, Dee, and Pat Wilson O'Leary. *A Guidebook for Cooperative Learning: Techniques for Creating More Effective Schools.* Holmes Beach, FL: Learning Publications, 1984.

> A practical guide to help teachers implement cooperative learning techniques in the classroom.

Johnson, David W., Roger T. Johnson, and Edythe Johnson Holubec. *Circles of Learning.* Alexandria, VA: Association for Supervision and Curriculum Development, 1984.

> Presents the case for cooperative learning in a concise and readable form. Reviews the research, outlines implementation strategies, and answers many questions.

Johnson, Sylvia A. *Beetles.* Lerner Natural Science series. Minneapolis, MN: Lerner, 1982.

> Offers a wealth of information on beetles. Another title in the series is *Snails,* also by Sylvia A. Johnson.

——. *Mosses.* Minneapolis, MN: Lerner, 1983.

> Informative text combined with good photographs.

Kneidel, Sally. *Pet Bugs.* New York: John Wiley, 1994.

> Shows how to catch and care for a variety of insects, including the Bess beetle.

Kramer, David C. *Animals in the Classroom.* New York: Addison-Wesley, 1989.

> A source book for elementary and middle school teachers interested in keeping a variety of small animals in the classroom.

Lingelbach, Jenepher. *Hands-On Nature: Information and Activities for Exploring the Environment with Children.* Woodstock, VT: Vermont Institute of Natural Science, 1986.

> Nature activities for grades K-6. Explores the natural world and the many interrelationships within it.

National Gardening Association. *Grow Lab: A Complete Guide to Gardening in the Classroom.* West Hartford, CT: Knox Parks Foundation, 1988.

> Based on a school gardening program in Hartford, Connecticut. A complete guide for keeping a garden in the classroom.

Nickelsburg, Janet. *Nature Activities for Early Childhood.* Reading, MA: Addison-Wesley, 1976.

> A source book of activities in which students observe nature, from spiders to rocks.

Ocone, Lynn, and Eve Pranis. *The Youth Gardening Book.* Burlington, VT: National Gardening Association, 1983.

> Everything you need to know about starting an outdoor garden project with your students.

Simon, Seymour. *Pets in a Jar.* New York: Puffin, 1975.

> A simple how-to book for keeping pets (from hydras to toads) in jars.

**Resources for the Class: Observing**

Aliki. *My Five Senses.* New York: Harper Trophy, 1989.

> A "Let's-Read-and-Find-Out" book describing the five senses and how we use them to perceive the world around us.

Baylor, Byrd, and Peter Parnall. *The Other Way to Listen.* New York: Charles Scribner, 1978.

> A read-aloud book. Encourages children to take the time to listen to the world around them as they experience nature.

Hoban, Tana. *Look! Look! Look!* New York: Greenwillow Books, 1988.

> Helps children turn the unknown into the familiar by using the sense of sight.

Pearce, Q. L., and W. J. Pearce. *In the Forest.* Nature's Footprints series. Englewood Cliffs, NJ: Silver Press, 1990.

> How to track the footprints of 10 animals and build observational skills. Part of a read-aloud picture book series.

**Resources for the Class: Habitats**

Cristini, Ermano, and Luigi Puricelli. *In the Woods.* Saxonville, MA: Picture Book Studio, 1983.

> Illustrates life in the woods and challenges children to identify a whole object by examining only a part.

————. *In the Pond.* Saxonville, MA: Picture Book Studio, 1984.

> This wordless book illustrates the living things of marshy wetlands and what happens above, around, and beneath the water of a pond. Companion book to *In the Woods,* also by Ermano Cristini and Luigi Puricelli.

Curran, Eileen. *Life in the Forest.* New York: Troll Associates, 1985.

> Asks children to look closely to see the organisms of the forest. For beginning readers to read independently. The companion book in this set is *Life in the Pond,* also by Eileen Curran.

Fife, Dale H. *The Vacant Lot.* San Francisco: Little Brown, 1991.

> Harry Hale has decided to sell his vacant lot. But when he decides to visit it, he discovers that it is far from empty.

Guiberson, Brenda Z. *Cactus Hotel.* New York: Holt, 1991.

> A story about a saguaro cactus and the animals that make their home in it.

Kalman, Bobbie. *Wonderful Water*. The Primary Ecology series. New York: Crabtree, 1992.

Includes a study of pond habitats. The books in this series are filled with activities that help teach children how to use what they already know about the environment to actively participate in solving problems they see around them.

Mazer, Anne. *The Salamander Room*. New York: Knopf, 1991.

A boy finds an orange salamander, takes it home, and tries to turn his room into the perfect home for it.

Parker, Nancy Winslow. *Working Frog*. New York: Greenwillow, 1992.

Winston the bullfrog tells the story of his capture and new life at the reptile house in a zoo.

Rius, Maria, and J. M. Parramon. *Life on the Land*. New York: Barrons, 1987.

Describes the planting of a tiny tree in a forest by the children who cared for it at home. Highlights the living things that keep the tree company. Part of a series on habitats. Other titles in the series are *Life Underground*, *Life in the Air*, and *Life in the Sea*, all by Maria Rius and J. M. Parramon.

Romanova, Natalia. *Once There Was a Tree*. New York: Dial Books, 1985.

A Russian tale of a tree split by lightning, leaving only a stump, and the life on and around the stump as seasons change.

## Resources for the Class: Seeds and Plants

Aliki. *Corn Is Maize: The Gift of the Indians*. New York: Harper and Row, 1976.

The story of how American Indians found and developed corn and later shared this treasure with the new settlers.

Althea. *Tree*. White Plains, NY: Longman Group, 1988.

From a series of life cycle nature books for young children. Another title in the series is *Flowers*, by Althea.

Back, Christine. *Bean and Plant*. Stopwatch series. Morristown, NJ: Silver Burdett, 1986.

Documents the growth of a lima bean plant.

Behn, Harry. *Trees*. New York: Henry Holt, 1977.

An eloquent poem about the importance of trees to our world.

Brown, Marc. *Your First Garden Book*. London: Little, Brown, 1981.

More than 20 ideas for indoor and outdoor plant projects, along with whimsical illustrations.

Bjork, Christina, and Lena Anderson. *Linnea's Windowsill Garden*. Translated by Joan Sandin. New York: R & S Books, 1989.

Linnea takes children on a tour of her indoor garden and inspires them to start their own.

Berger, Melvin. *All about Seeds.* New York: Scholastic, 1992.

> Text mixed with activities to inform children about seeds and engage them in collecting, planting, and cooking them.

Carle, Eric. *The Tiny Seed.* Saxonville, MA: Picture Book Studio, 1990.

> Simple text explains the life cycle of a flower through the adventures of a tiny seed.

Challand, Helen J. *Plants without Seeds.* New True Book science series. Chicago: Children's Press, 1986.

> Examines the characteristics of simple plants that do not have seeds, including mosses.

Curran, Eileen. *Look at a Tree.* New York: Troll Associates, 1985.

> Asks the reader to look closely at a tree to see what lives and plays on it. For beginning readers to read independently.

De Bourgoing, Pascale. *The Tree.* First Discovery Book series. New York: Scholastic, 1989.

> Beautiful overlapping illustrations help young children watch a seed sprout, a tree blossom, or a fruit ripen. Another title in the series is *Fruit,* also by Pascale De Bourgoing.

Ehlert, Lois. *Red Leaf, Yellow Leaf.* New York: Harcourt Brace Jovanovich, 1991.

> The story of a sugar maple tree and the child who planted it.

Gibbons, Gail. *The Seasons of Arnold's Apple Tree.* New York: Harcourt Brace Jovanovich, 1984.

> As the seasons pass, Arnold enjoys a variety of activities surrounding his apple tree.

———. *From Seed to Plant.* New York: Holiday House, 1991.

> Reveals how seeds are formed and grow into plants.

Gordon, Sharon. *Trees.* New York: Troll Associates, 1983.

> Walks the reader through the woods to look at a variety of trees. For beginning readers to read independently.

Heller, Ruth. *The Reason for a Flower.* New York: Putnam Publishing Group, 1983.

> A wealth of information about plants, pollination, and plant products. This book includes the *Rafflesia.*

———. *Plants that Never Ever Bloom.* New York: Scholastic, 1984.

> Rhyming story about plants that do not flower, including mosses.

Ikeda, Daisaku. *The Cherry Tree.* New York: Knopf, 1992.

> Taichi and Yumiko have lost their home and father to a war. They care for an aged, gnarled cherry tree that has not bloomed in years and come to terms with their losses.

Jaspersohn, William. *How the Forest Grew.* New York: Morrow, 1992.

Traces the development of a mature forest.

Jennings, Terry. *Seeds.* Junior Science series. New York: Gloucester Press, 1990.

Combines simple text and colorful illustrations to show how a seed grows. Also includes simple activities.

Jordan, Helen J. *How a Seed Grows.* New York: Harper Trophy, 1992.

Combines planting activities with text to explain how a kidney bean grows.

Kuchalla, Susan. *All about Seeds.* New York: Troll Associates, 1985.

A book about seeds for beginning readers to read independently.

Lauber, Patricia. *Seeds: Pop Stick Glide.* New York: Crown, 1981.

Beautiful photographs depicting a variety of seeds.

Lionni, Leo. *A Busy Year.* New York: Knopf, 1992.

Two mice care for a tree through the months.

McMillan, Bruce. *Growing Colors.* New York: William Morrow, 1994.

A perfect book for young gardeners. Colorful fruits and vegetables are shown in full-page photographs, each with a smaller photograph showing the whole plant. A single word of text appears on each page.

Merrill, Claire. *A Seed Is a Promise.* New York: Scholastic, 1973.

Simple book that tells all about seeds and their promise of life.

Miner, O. Irene Severy. *Plants We Know.* New True Book series. Chicago: Children's Press, 1983.

Uses simple text to introduce different kinds of plants, their parts, how they grow, and their benefits to humans.

Mitgutsch, Ali. *From Tree to Table.* Minneapolis, MN: Carolrhoda Books, 1981.

Part of a wonderful series of start-to-finish books. Other titles in the series are *From Wood to Paper, From Seed to Pear,* and *From Beet to Sugar,* all by Ali Mitgutsch.

Podendorf, Illa. *Trees.* New True Book series. Chicago: Children's Press, 1982.

Uses simple text to introduce parts of a tree, different kinds of trees, and their place in the environment.

Sekido, Isamu. *Fruit, Roots, and Fungi: Plants We Eat.* Science All Around You series. Minneapolis, MN: Lerner, 1993.

Good introduction to the abundance of food we get from plants.

Selsam, Millicent E., and Joyce Hunt. *A First Look at the World of Plants.* First Look At series. New York: Walker, 1978.

The text encourages the beginning reader to observe the characteristics of plants.

Sobol, Harriet L. *A Book of Vegetables*. New York: Dodd, Mead, 1984.

A look at 14 favorite vegetables and how they grow.

Steele, Mary Q. *Anna's Garden Songs*. New York: Scholastic, 1989.

Poems about common garden vegetables and herbs.

Thomson, Ruth. *Trees*. Usborne First Nature series. Tulsa, OK: EDC Publishing, 1990.

Filled with information on trees.

Tresselt, Alvin. *The Gift of the Tree*. New York: Lothrop, Lee and Shepard Books, 1992.

Describes the role of an oak tree in the cycle of nature. Complemented by beautiful paintings.

Udry, Janice May. *A Tree Is Nice*. New York: Harper Trophy, 1956.

A Caldicott Medal book, this book is a wonderful discussion starter.

Wilkes, Angela. *My First Garden Book*. New York: Knopf, 1992.

Features simple gardening projects, from collecting seeds to growing a miniature desert garden.

## Resources for the Class: Animals

Barrett, Judi. *Animals Should Definitely Not Wear Clothing*. New York: Scholastic, 1970.

This humorous book illustrates why animals should not try to wear clothes.

Bernhard, Emery. *Ladybug*. New York: Holiday House, 1992.

The complete story of one of the most loved beetles. Voted best nonfiction book for younger youth by the Young Entomologist's Society.

Clements, Andrew. *Big Al*. New York: Yoshi, 1988.

A good story to illustrate that what is ugly is not necessarily bad.

De Bourgoing, Pascale. *The Ladybug and Other Insects*. First Discovery Book series. New York: Scholastic, 1989.

Beautiful overlapping illustrations show the life cycle of the ladybug.

Eastman, David. *What Is a Fish?* New York: Troll Associates, 1982.

Describes a variety of fish. For beginning readers to read independently.

Fisher, Aileen. *When It Comes to Bugs*. New York: Harper and Row, 1986.

Sixteen original poems show the world from the bug's point of view.

Himmelman, John. *The Ups and Downs of Simpson Snail*. New York: Dutton, 1989.

Good beginning reader.

Hoberman, Mary Ann. *A House Is a House for Me.* New York: Penguin Group, 1982.

Lists in rhyme the dwellings of a variety of things.

Kilpatrick, Cathy. *Creepy Crawlies.* Usborne First Nature series. London: Usborne, 1982.

Filled with information on insects and other tiny animals.

Koss, Amy Goldman. *City Critters around the World.* Los Angeles: Price Stern Sloan, 1991.

Takes the reader around the globe and shows how various animals adapt to city life.

Lionni, Leo. *Biggest House in the World.* New York: Knopf, 1987.

Tells the story of a snail who wants to trade in its shell for a bigger and bigger "house" to live in.

————. *Fish Is Fish.* New York: Knopf, 1987.

When Fish's friend, the tadpole, turns into a frog and leaves the pond, Fish imagines what life would be like outside the pond.

Mitchell, Joni. *Both Sides Now.* New York: Scholastic, 1992.

Features two caterpillars who demonstrate how both clouds and life appear differently when viewed from different perspectives. The message is that change is an important part of life.

McKissack, Patricia C. *A Million Fish . . . More or Less.* New York: Knopf, 1992.

A boy gets a chance to tell his own version of a bayou tale when he goes fishing.

Nash, Pamela. *The Snail.* See How It Grows series. Columbus, OH: Modern Curriculum Press, 1983.

A simple book for beginning readers.

National Geographic Society Staff, ed. Pop-up Action Books series. Washington, DC: National Geographic Society, 1982.

This book series includes *Animal Homes* and *At the Zoo.*

National Geographic Society Staff, ed. Books for Young Explorers series. Washington, DC: National Geographic Society, 1991.

Beautiful books about nature for beginning readers. Titles include *Dinnertime for Animals* and *Animal Clowns.*

Olesen, Jens. *Snail.* Stopwatch Book series. Englewood Cliffs, NJ: Silver Burdett Press, 1986.

Combines excellent photographs and simple text.

Pallotta, Jerry. *The Icky Bug Alphabet Book.* Watertown, MA: Charlesbridge, 1986.

Introduces a variety of strange insects and bugs.

Podendorf, Illa. *Insects.* New True Book series. Chicago: Children's Press, 1981.

> Uses simple text to describe insects.

Rockwell, Anne. *The Story Snail.* New York: Macmillan, 1987.

> A ready-to-read book about a snail who gives a boy 100 stories to tell.

Segaloff, Nat, and Paul Erickson. *Fish Tales.* New York: Sterling, 1990.

> Describes the variety of swimming creatures in a range of habitats from the Arctic to small thermal pools.

Spier, Peter. *People.* New York: Bantam Doubleday Dell Publishing Group, 1980.

> Illustrates the diversity among the peoples of the world.

Ryder, Joanne. *The Snail's Spell.* New York: Puffin Books, 1982.

> Invites children to imagine how it feels to be a snail.

Seymour, Peter. *Insects: A Close-up Look.* New York: Macmillan, 1984.

> This pop-up book introduces children to the world of insects.

Singaporean Children. *Animal Poems.* Edited by Pugalenthi. Singapore: V J Times, 1992.

> Animal poems written by children between the ages of 9 and 13. Invites children to express themselves through writing.

Spohn, David. *Nate's Treasure.* New York: Lothrop, Lee and Shepard Books, 1991.

> When a fight between a family dog and a skunk results in the death of the skunk, a young boy experiences the cycle of nature.

Stadler, John. *Snail Saves the Day.* New York: Harper Trophy, 1988.

> Humorous book for beginning readers to read independently.

Still, John. *Amazing Beetles.* Eyewitness Juniors series. New York: Knopf, 1991.

> Filled with information about amazing beetles and photographs of them. The series also includes *Amazing Fish,* by Mary Ling.

Watts, Barrie. *Keeping Minibeasts: Beetles.* Keeping Minibeasts series. New York: Franklin Watts, 1989.

> Uses photographs and simple text to introduce children to beetles.

Wildsmith, Brian. *Fishes.* New York: Oxford University Press, 1989.

> Beautiful paintings with captions identifying the groups of fish.

Yorinks, Arthur. *Louis the Fish.* New York: Farrar, Straus & Giroux, 1991.

> A Reading Rainbow book about an unhappy butcher who goes through an amazing transformation.

### Resources for the Class: Death

Manson, Christopher. *The Tree in the Wood.* New York: North-South Books, 1994.

> This adaptation of a classic circular rhyme encompasses an entire circle of change and rebirth.

Mellonie, Bryan, and Robert Ingpen. *Lifetimes: The Beautiful Way to Explain Death to Children.* New York: Bantam, 1983.

> Deals with the sensitive topic of death by explaining about beginnings and endings.

Viorst, Judith. *The Tenth Good Thing About Barney.* New York: Atheneum, 1971.

> A sensitive story about Barney the cat and how everyone acted and felt when he died. It portays death as a natural part of life.

Wilhelm, Hans. *I'll Always Love You.* New York: Crown, 1985.

> Helps children deal with their sadness when they lose a loved one.

### Resources for the Class: Films and Videocassettes

*At Home With Zoos.* 15 min. Washington, DC: National Geographic Society, 1992. Videocassette or film.

> Children learn how zoos attempt to meet the needs of animals by copying their natural environments. For grades K–3.

*Fish.* 16 min. Washington, DC: National Geographic Society, 1985. Videocassette or film.

> Close-up and slow-motion photography showing the anatomy of a goldfish and how the fish moves. For grades K–3.

*Living or Non-Living?* 16 min. Washington, DC: National Geographic Society, 1986. Videocassette or film.

> Explores the differences between living and nonliving things by emphasizing the characteristics of life. For grades K–3.

*Plant or Animal?* 15 min. Washington, DC: National Geographic Society, 1986. Videocassette or film.

> Shows the major differences between the plant and animal kingdoms.

### Resources for the Class: Computer Software

Learn about Animals. Pleasantville, New York: Sunburst, 1992.

> Students investigate animals' homes, food, and babies, as well as size and movement. They locate animals, create real or imaginary animals, and write their own animal stories.

Learn about Plants. Pleasantville, New York: Sunburst, 1992.

> Students plant an on-screen garden and watch their seedlings grow. They identify the parts of plants and discover how plants help people.

Learn about Insects. Pleasantville, New York: Sunburst, 1992.

Students identify insects and their parts, sequence their growth, and match them with homes and food. An on-disk field guide helps students move through the activities.

# Tips on Receiving and Maintaining Live Materials

## Woodland Plants: Tree Seedlings and Moss

**Materials**

    Plant mister

**Procedure**

The tree seedlings and moss will arrive together. The seedlings will be in plastic planter cups and wrapped in moist paper. The moss will come in four plastic containers.

When the plants arrive, open the packaging enough to give the plants some air. Keep the soil around the seedling moist but not wet, and mist the whole moss mat. Store the plants in indirect light.

When the tree seedlings get too tall for the terraria, you can keep them in your class for an extended period of time. Transplant them into 15- to 20-cm (6- to 8-in) pots. Consult with a nursery about caring for the seedlings.

**Note:** Most of the organisms you receive should be in good condition. When organisms are shipped, however, it is possible that some may arrive damaged or dead. If this happens, contact your supplier immediately.

## Woodland Animals: Pill Bugs

**Materials**

1   holding pail and lid, with 2.5 cm (1 in) of damp soil
    Leaf litter and a piece of bark or twigs
    Lettuce or a slice of potato for food

**Procedure**

Pill bugs are very easy to keep. Carefully punch a few air holes in the lid of the holding pail with a sharp scissors or pushpin.

Put about 2.5 cm (1 in) of the leftover soil from Lesson 4 in the holding pail. Moisten the soil if it has dried out.

Open the shipping container. The pill bugs will be shipped with a moist paper towel. You will find most of the pill bugs in the paper towel. Put the towel and pill bugs in the pail and add the leaf litter, bark, and lettuce or potato.

Put the lid on the holding pail. You can store the holding pail just about anywhere that is not too cold or too hot. The pill bugs do not require light.

Check the pill bugs daily to make sure the surface of the soil is damp. Also replace any moldy food.

**Maintaining the pill bugs in the classroom**

The terrarium contains everything the pill bugs need to live. Just be sure the moisture level is appropriate (see Lesson 4) and that it contains leaf litter and bark or twigs. The pill bugs will spend most of the time under or in the moss and near the twigs and leaf litter. Students will have to observe closely to see them. Students may lift the terrarium lid and gently poke around to locate the pill bugs, but they should be careful not to disturb the living plants. Students can also put in a slice of potato to lure the pill bugs into view.

# Woodland Animals: Bess Beetles

**Materials**

1   holding pail and lid, with 5 cm (2 in) of damp soil
    Wood chunks
1   scissors

**Procedure**

Carefully punch a few air holes in the lid of the holding pail with the scissors.

Put a 5-cm (2-in) layer of damp soil on the bottom of the holding pail.

Open the shipping container. Gently tip the beetles into the holding pail. (The beetles will probably squeak, since they are being disturbed.)

Check to see if there are wood chunks in the holding pail. If not, add a couple. Put the lid on the pail. Store it with the holding pails of pill bugs. The Bess beetles should not stay in the holding pail for more than a week.

**Maintaining the Bess beetles in the classroom**

Add a wood chunk to each terrarium. Place it on the opposite side from the tree seedling and moss. Keeping the wood away from the living plants will deter the beetles from digging under the seedling and moss and disturbing the seedling's roots. The beetles will dig under the wood and, generally, remain there. Add more wood when you observe that the existing chunk is almost chewed up. Keep the wood chunks moist by misting them once or twice a day.

The terrarium now contains all that the Bess beetles need to live. As with the pill bugs, just check the moisture level of the terrarium daily. Students may lift the terrarium lid to discover where the beetles prefer to be.

# Woodland Animals: Millipedes

**Materials**

1   holding pail and lid, with 5 cm (2 in) of damp soil
    Leaf litter
1   scissors
1   pair of disposable plastic gloves
    Pieces of lettuce or mushrooms

**Procedure**

Before you transfer the millipedes from the shipping container to the holding pail, use the scissors to punch a few air holes in the lid of the holding pail.

Put a 5-cm (2-in) layer of damp soil on the bottom of the holding pail. Add some leaf litter.

Open the shipping container and gently tip the millipedes into the pail. You can store them anywhere that is not too cold or too hot.

If you need to keep the millipedes in the pail for more than a day, give them a small handful of fresh mushrooms or lettuce to feed on.

### Maintaining the millipedes in the classroom

Add some decaying wood, bark, or more leaf litter to each terrarium. The millipedes will burrow into the soil or under the moss, seeking a dark, damp spot. Keep a supply of fresh mushrooms or lettuce in the school's refrigerator. Feed each millipede a few pieces every couple of days.

**Note:** When taken out of the security of a terrarium or other container, millipedes tend to defecate. On occasion, they may also give off a secretion from their stink glands. The secreted substance can cause mild irritation to mucous membranes (such as the eyes) or open cuts. In this event, immediately flush the area with water.

Whenever you or your students handle the millipedes, you will need to wear the plastic gloves provided in the kit. These disposable gloves should be worn only one time. Always make sure students wash their hands when they are finished observing and handling the millipedes.

## Freshwater Aquarium

Water is the single most important ingredient in an aquarium. The water you provide is crucial to the survival of the aquatic organisms. Before the organisms arrive, have ready either bottled spring water (not mineral water) or conditioned tap water. To prepare the conditioned water, fill two of the holding pails provided in the kit with tap water and dechlorinate it by following the directions on the tap-water conditioner. Let the water sit until it reaches room temperature. Replenish the conditioned water as you use it. Always keep some extra room-temperature conditioned water in the classroom.

**Note:** If you used all the pails to hold soil in Lessons 3 and 4, rinse them out with water only—do not use soap. Be sure to remove all soil debris or you will contaminate the aquarium.

## Freshwater Plants: *Elodea* and *Cabomba*

**Materials**        2   holding pails filled with conditioned water

**Procedure**        *Elodea* and *Cabomba* are easy to maintain. Open the shipping container immediately and place the *Elodea* in one pail and the *Cabomba* in the other. Place the uncovered holding pails in an area that gets bright light.

**Management Tip:** After Lesson 5, replenish the holding pails with conditioned water for the snails in Lesson 7 and then again for the guppies in Lesson 8. Also, keep one or two sprigs of the Elodea for the snail and guppy holding pails.

# Freshwater Animals: Snails

**Materials**

1   holding pail filled with conditioned water

**Procedure**

When the snails arrive, open the shipping container immediately to check their condition. The container will also hold some *Elodea*. You will find the snails on or around the *Elodea*. It is important to see to their needs immediately. During shipping, snails may have contaminated the environment close to the limits of their endurance.

Rinse off the snails in some of the extra conditioned water you have kept on hand in the classroom. Then place them in the holding pail until you are ready to distribute them to the class.

**Note:** It is strongly recommended that you teach Lessons 7 and 8 very soon after the arrival of the animals.

Provide an ample supply of food-—two pinches of fish food and a few sprigs of *Elodea*. This will probably be enough food for about a week.

Remove any dead snails. It is hard to tell if a snail is dead or alive. If the snail is floating for a long time or just lying on the bottom of the pail, pick it up. If it retracts into its shell you will know it is still alive. (See Appendix B for information on discussing birth and death.)

If you must hold the snails for more than a week before using them in Lesson 7, you will need to do the following at the end of the week:

- Pour off most of the dirty water and replace it with an equal amount of room-temperature conditioned water.

- Replenish the food supply.

- Remove any dead snails.

**Maintaining the snails in the classroom**

Once added to the aquaria, the snails have everything that they need to live.

# Freshwater Animals: Guppies

**Materials**

3   holding pails of conditioned water (about two-thirds full)
2   empty holding pails
2–3   sprigs of *Elodea* or *Cabomba*
1   dip net

**Procedure**

When the guppies arrive, they will be in two plastic bags—one with about eight males and one with about eight females. Unpack them immediately.

Open the tops and float each shipping bag in a separate holding pail of conditioned water for 20 to 30 minutes. The floating will prevent shock from a sudden temperature change.

Discard about one-fourth of the water from each bag and replace it with water from the third bucket. After 15 minutes, repeat this process. This helps the fish adjust to the pH of their new water. After another 15 minutes, slowly and carefully pour the fish and shipping water from the bags into the empty pails (keeping the males and females in separate pails). Then, with a dip net, gently transfer the guppies into the two holding pails of conditioned water (see Figure A-1). Again, remember to place the males and females in separate pails. Discard the shipping water.

**Figure A-1**

*Netting and releasing the guppy*

Until you are ready to use the guppies, store the holding pails in a safe place that is in indirect light, is not too hot or too cold, and is out of the children's view.

Feed the fish a day after they arrive. Put one pinch of food into the holding pail. If the fish eat it all immediately, add another pinch. All food should be eaten within five minutes.

If you must hold the guppies for more than a week before using them in Lesson 8, you will need to do the following at the end of the week:

- Use a clean cup to scoop off half the dirty water and replace it with an equal amount of room-temperature conditioned water.

- Remove any dead guppies.

**Maintaining guppies in the classroom**

Always have available a supply of room-temperature conditioned water to maintain the appropriate water level in the aquaria. A small pinch of food daily is enough for each aquarium.

Immediately remove any dead fish. If the class wants to watch a dead fish decompose, place one in a cup of water out of direct sunlight. (See Appendix B for more information on the birth and death of guppies.)

# Advisory on Releasing the Organisms

The National Science Resources Center advises against the release of any organism used in the Science and Technology for Children program. In some documented cases, environmental problems have resulted from the introduction of nonindigenous organisms. It is also illegal in many states to release organisms, even indigenous species, without a permit. The intention of these laws is protection of native wildlife and the environment.

The organisms used in this unit were thoroughly researched before they were selected. They are unlikely to harm local ecosystems. Nevertheless, their release might encourage your students to release other organisms that could cause harm to native wildlife and local ecosystems. If you have any questions about releasing organisms in your area, contact your state or local environmental conservation agency.

Once you complete the unit, there are several things you can do with the organisms.

- Continue to maintain them in your classroom.

- Donate them to a pet shop, zoo, botanical garden, or greenhouse.

- Donate them to another classroom or to another school's science department.

- With parental permission, let your students adopt them and take them home.

- As a last resort, biologists suggest that you place the organisms in a sealed container, freeze them, and bury them.

If you give the organisms to students or to other groups, please make them aware of this advisory.

# Discussing Death and Birth

**Death**

Over the course of this unit, some of the animals and plants are likely to die. While this experience may be difficult for some students, it is also an opportunity for them to begin thinking about death as a natural part of the life cycle of all living things.

If you need to discuss the death of animals and plants with your students, the article "Teaching the Toughest Lesson—About Death," which begins on pg. 220 of this appendix, will give you some helpful background information. In addition, the Bibliography has a section of children's books on the subject of death.

### What to Do with Dead Animals

Remove any dead snails or guppies with the dip net. If you would like the class to observe their decomposition, put them in a cup with water. (If you leave dead animals in the tank they may foul the water.) Likewise, remove any dead woodland animals and put these in a cup if you would like your class to observe decomposition.

Dead fish, beetles, pill bugs, and millipedes are easy to notice, but dead snails are not. If a snail is lying on its sides on the tank bottom or floating for long periods of time, remove it and check to see if it responds by retracting into its shell. If no sign of life is evident, place the snail in a cup of tank water for a day. Have the students watch for movement.

## Teaching the Toughest Lesson–About Death

By David J. Schonfeld and Murray Kappelman

Death is a topic most teachers would rather not discuss, let alone teach. It is easy to understand why surveys show that very few elementary-school teachers deal with the subject in any planned manner in their classes. Death is an uncomfortable topic to think about, so we look for reasons not to teach it. We rationalize by thinking inwardly, "How can I even begin to explain something to my class of small children that I don't understand well myself?"

What we may fail to realize is how much greater a disadvantage young pupils have when coming to grips with this terrifying reality. They may lack an understanding of even the most basic concepts about what it means when someone they know dies. They are unable, then, to understand what has occurred and to begin to deal with the loss.

Can children learn this type of information without our assistance? Not easily. Parents and other significant adults in their lives (including teachers) often unsuccessfully attempt to protect them from the experience and the knowledge. But what these well-meaning adults fail to grasp is that virtually all children, by the time they reach school age, have had some experience with death that is significant to them. Avoiding the subject in school and at home only creates more mystery and fear.

Do these experiences involve the kinds of losses an adult would appreciate? Not always. One girl, for example, raised her hand in a school assembly to share a significant personal-loss story with the group. She had found a spider in her bedroom, and without her family's knowledge, had raised it as a pet, bringing it crumbs to eat and watching it spinning its web. One day a family member found the spider and killed it. As the girl recounted this story, she began to cry. The loss for her was far more significant than her family could have realized. Such "minor" but significant losses occur regularly in children's lives.

Yet the information children are given about death is almost invariably incorrect. Television and children's stories are full of references to death, but typically depict it inaccurately—characters die and later return to life with regularity. Parents and other adults often try and replace deceased pets and give children false assurances, such as telling them that they will never die. It is not surprising, then, that children do not learn these basic facts easily without added guidance. Teachers, in fact, may be their only source of correct information.

We can prepare children for later losses by teaching them the information before they need to use it. As with all topics, we have to teach children information prior to the time it is needed, to allow time for mastery and acquisition of skills. If we wait till a child is faced with the death of a close relative or friend, we have waited too long.

Through our work with schools, we have found that teachers who are armed with insight and information feel freer to allow discussions about death to occur

Reprinted with permission from *Education Week.* This article appeared in the March 4, 1992, issue of *Education Week* (vol. 11, no. 24).

David J. Schonfeld is assistant professor of pediatrics at the Yale University School of Medicine. Murray Kappelman is professor of pediatrics and psychiatry and director of the Division of Behavioral and Developmental Pediatrics at the University of Maryland School of Medicine.

in the classrooms. Many, moreover, are pleasantly surprised by how well each instruction is received, and how comfortable the children become with the discussion. We may not be able to answer all of children's questions about death, but we can certainly provide them with some of the most basic concepts as a foundation for their future. These include the knowledge that:

**Death is irreversible.** Children need to understand that death is a permanent phenomenon. There is no return or recovery from death, no matter how much we may wish otherwise. The child who expects the deceased to return, as if he had gone away on a trip, may be angry at the one who has died for not coming back, or even bothering to call. If the child does not appreciate the irreversibility of death, then there is also no reason to begin to detach personal ties to the deceased, a necessary first step in the mourning process.

**All life functions cease at the time of death.** Children must understand that all of the activities of body and mind—eating, breathing, cognition, sensation, and so on—cease completely at the time of death. Young children who do not understand this may wish to bury pet food with their dead dog, or may be unduly concerned about a deceased relative's being hungry, cold, or in pain. They will tell you that dead people don't see well because it is dark underground, or that they can't move "as much" because they are restrained by the coffin.

Failure to understand this concept often leads to a preoccupation with the physical suffering of the dead person. In one assembly of 4th graders, three of the children had experienced the death of a parent or guardian in the previous 12 to 18 months. All three had been to a wake where the casket was open and all of them had thought, at some point, that they saw the body move. Because of their incomplete understanding of this concept of death's finality, all three children still had recurrent nightmares that their parent or guardian was, in some way, "buried alive," fighting to get out of the grave. Merely explaining the concept to these children helped them by reducing this unnecessary fear—a fear that is unfortunately augmented by some horror movies and sensational stories in supermarket tabloids.

**There are true causes why living things die.** The child must develop a realistic understanding of the true causes of death. Young children, who lack this understanding, will often reach the conclusion that bad thoughts or unrelated actions (or omissions) were responsible for the death of a loved one. This leads to excessive guilt that is very difficult for the child to resolve. It is almost universal for those close to someone who has died to question whether there was something they did, or failed to do, that was related to the death. But most adults, after considerable introspection, will correctly reach the conclusion that they were not, in fact, responsible. That is because they know the real reason for the death.

Children who lack an understanding of the true causes of death, are not able to reach this conclusion; they are left instead with little as an alternative to self-blame. As one bright 2nd grader matter-of-factly stated: "My brother died of sudden infant death syndrome because I went away to camp that day." Only after a discussion of the true causes of death was the boy able to absolve himself of his perceived responsibility for his brother's death.

**Death is inevitable.** The child must learn that death is a natural phenomenon; every living thing eventually dies. Children who feel that significant individuals, such as themselves or their parents, are immortal are indicating their lack of appreciation of the inevitability of death. Parents and other adults will often question why young children need to know "this harsh fact of life" at young ages. What harm, they may argue, is there in protecting their children from this reality for "as long as possible"? The problem is that death is a reality; someone or something of importance to the child will eventually die, and usually before the parent feels it is time to acknowledge this "harsh reality." If the child does not view death as inevitable, then he or she is likely to view death as a form of punishment, either for actions or thoughts of the deceased or of the child. This, in turn, leads to excessive guilt and shame that makes coping and adjustment to the loss very difficult.

Studies have shown that even very young children are capable of understanding these concepts about death. Most children, in fact, learn them between the ages of 5 and 7. Education has been shown to even further advance the understanding of the young child (that is, pre-kindergarten through 2nd grade). But teachers need not create formal death-education classes in the primary and elementary grades. Instead, we recommend that they make a conscious effort to integrate information about death into existing curricula, and that they take advantage of spontaneous class discussions and naturally occurring events, such as when a student finds a dead goldfish in the class fish tank or a dead bug on the playground.

Children have many questions about death and are eager to discuss it once the topic has been broached by a caring adult. One child, on hearing that we would be talking about death in her class, pulled out a picture she had drawn earlier that day of an elaborate graveyard scene and was eager to discuss it. Her teacher seemed surprised by the picture, but such drawings are common among young children and need not be cause for alarm. In fact, young children often find the topic fascinating.

Teachers may also wish to take advantage of the many excellent stories and videos dealing with death that can be found in the school system or at local libraries. Educational materials should be selected that present the information clearly and accurately and that reinforce the relevant concepts in a manner that is developmentally appropriate for the intended group.

It is reasonable for teachers to be concerned that when they first begin discussing death in their classroom children will challenge them with questions they fear are inappropriate—or perhaps impossible to answer. Questions involving religious beliefs actually occur infrequently in the primary and early elementary grades. When they do, such questions as "When you die, don't you go to heaven to live with God?" can easily be answered with statements such as "No one knows for sure what happens when someone dies; some people believe in a special place called heaven where they believe God lives." The children can, and should, be directed back to their parents and family if they want further information touching on religious beliefs.

At times, children will also ask questions for which no good answer is available, such as "But why did my dog have to die so young? It just isn't fair." Such questions should be answered honestly, reflecting the lack of an adequate explanation.

Other children, in the later elementary grades, may ask questions relating to details of body preparation, burial, and decomposition that may make the teacher initially uncomfortable. In one assembly of 4th graders, several children wanted to know why the eyes remained closed during the wake and funeral. Unsatisfied by simple assurance that the body was prepared so that they would not open, they persisted with this line of inquiry, reflecting their age-appropriate curiosity. Once informed that the eyelids were sewn closed, they moved quickly onto new questions, with little reaction other than a brief, "Oh, gross."

In fact, children of this age group are able to provide much more vivid and unsettling images drawn from their own imaginations and supplemented by exposure to graphic horror films.

Most children will not become upset by these discussions. But for an occasional child, the teacher's willingness to talk about death may provide the opportunity for expressing feelings about prior or current crises, some related to death, some not. Children have used these occasions, for example, to talk about their concerns regarding their parent's drug abuse, ongoing physical abuse in the home, or unresolved feelings about prior losses. Teachers will need to be prepared to deal with such situations when they arise, and they should know about appropriate resources for children within their school and community.

Teachers must remember that the child who is upset during such discussions is invariably expressing feelings and emotions that existed prior to the discussion; the teacher's willingness to "hear" these feelings is the reason that the child is able to express them. The discussion did not cause the upset, but only allowed its expression, a needed first step to its resolution.

The intensity of the discussions should be monitored, however, and when it seems appropriate the conversation should be refocused on positive coping techniques (such as talking to people, drawing pictures) and on sources of support within the home (emphasizing parents), school, and community. Children can then raise their hand to share with the group about when their dog died and be asked in turn "What helped you feel better then?" Other students will eagerly volunteer activities that made them feel better when they were sad. An individual student who appears to have more to discuss than is appropriate for the classroom setting can be approached individually after class.

Teachers will be amazed though, at the capacity of even very young children to tolerate sad emotions in a caring context and to assist their peers. In one 2nd-grade class, a boy began to cry during a film because he was reminded of the death of his pet dog a year earlier. When the film was stopped, the boy insisted on remaining for its conclusion and asked that it be restarted. Without any prompting, a classmate brought him a box of tissue and another child put his arm around the boy's shoulder.

In a pre-kindergarten class, a girl who had not been present for the class's discussion about death the week before returned from the weekend and told a friend that her grandmother had died. The teacher was proud to overhear the friend offer support and advice on coping techniques: "You could try drawing a picture of your grandmother," the child said. "Sometimes that helps you feel better."

**Birth**

Both guppies and snails may give birth sometime during the unit. In this event, you may find the following information helpful.

### Guppies

Guppies are live-bearers. If one of the classroom guppies gives birth, you will need to separate the babies from the adults. You can place them in the extra class tank to create a nursery. Otherwise, the adults will eat many of them. The babies are so small that the net may damage them, so use the ladle to get a scoop of water containing the babies and add it to the nursery tank. (In this instance, you can mix a small amount of water from the two tanks to transfer the babies safely.) Feed the babies on the same schedule you follow for the adults.

If adults have died in one of the aquaria, you can use that one as the nursery. Or, if some of the adults have died, transfer a few to other tanks to create more breeding pairs. Students can observe the growth of newborn guppies or snails and also can compare newborns with older guppies.

The surprise appearance of young fish is an exciting event for children, and it presents a good opportunity for you to discuss the ways the young resemble their parents. Ask the following questions to encourage students to compare the young fish with the adults:

- Are they the same size?

- Do both have fins?

- Do both have eyes?

- Do they swim and eat like each other?

- Can the young fish live without their mothers?

- Where do the young fish spend most of their time?

- How many young fish are in the nursery tank?

- How many young fish and young snails are there altogether?

### Snails

Snail eggs will have a better chance of survival if they are in tanks without fish. If the egg masses are disappearing, the fish may be eating them. Discuss with the class possible reasons why the eggs have disappeared.

You can carefully move egg masses into the nursery tank. Try to move egg masses that are attached to plants or gently scrape some off the sides of a tank.

To launch a discussion on the birth of snails, try the following questions:

- How many snail eggs are in one mass?

- Do adult snails pay attention to the eggs?

- Do snail eggs need to be in water to hatch?

- Do baby snails leave the water?

- Do adult snails take care of baby snails?

**Blackline Masters**

This appendix contains blackline master outlines for the stuffed animals mentioned in several lesson extensions.

# Snail

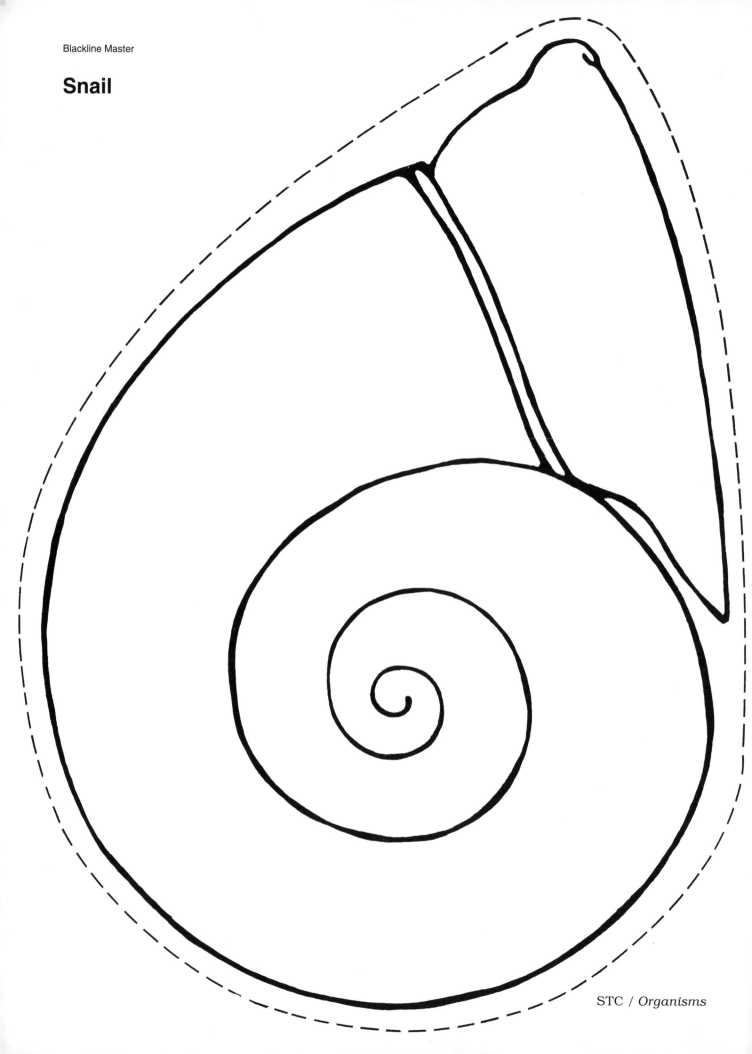

# Guppy

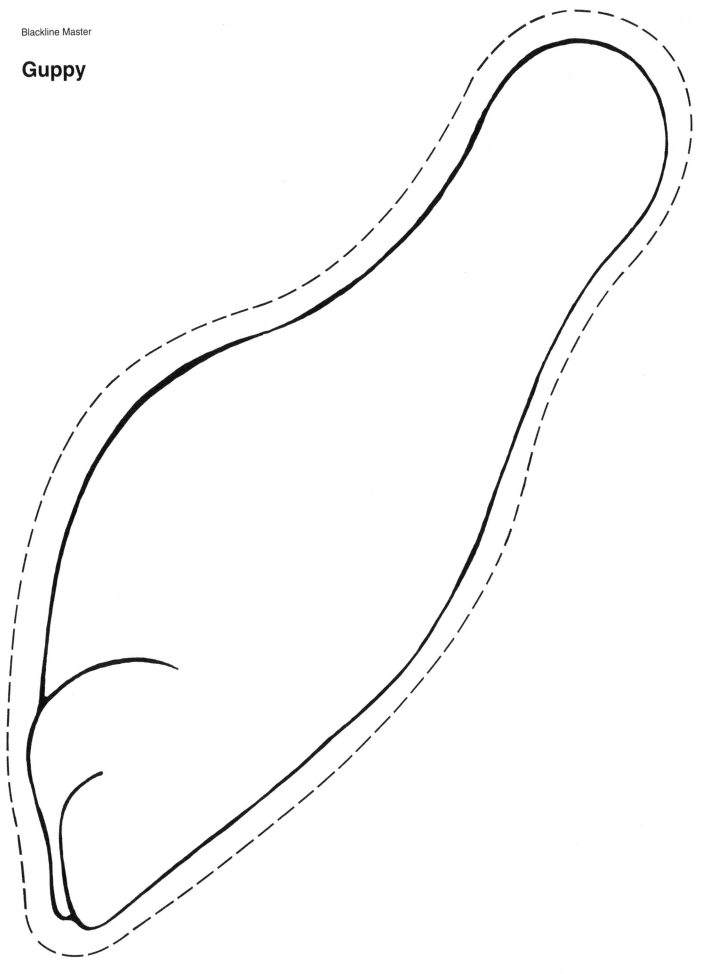

# Pill Bug

# Bess Beetle

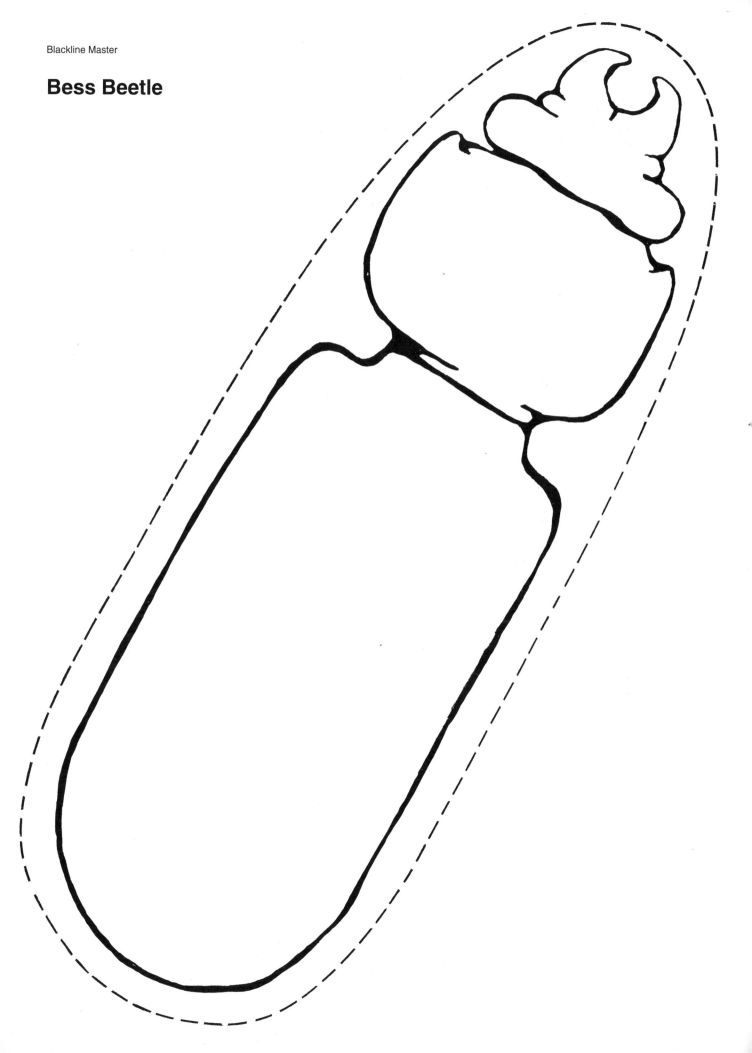

# Millipede

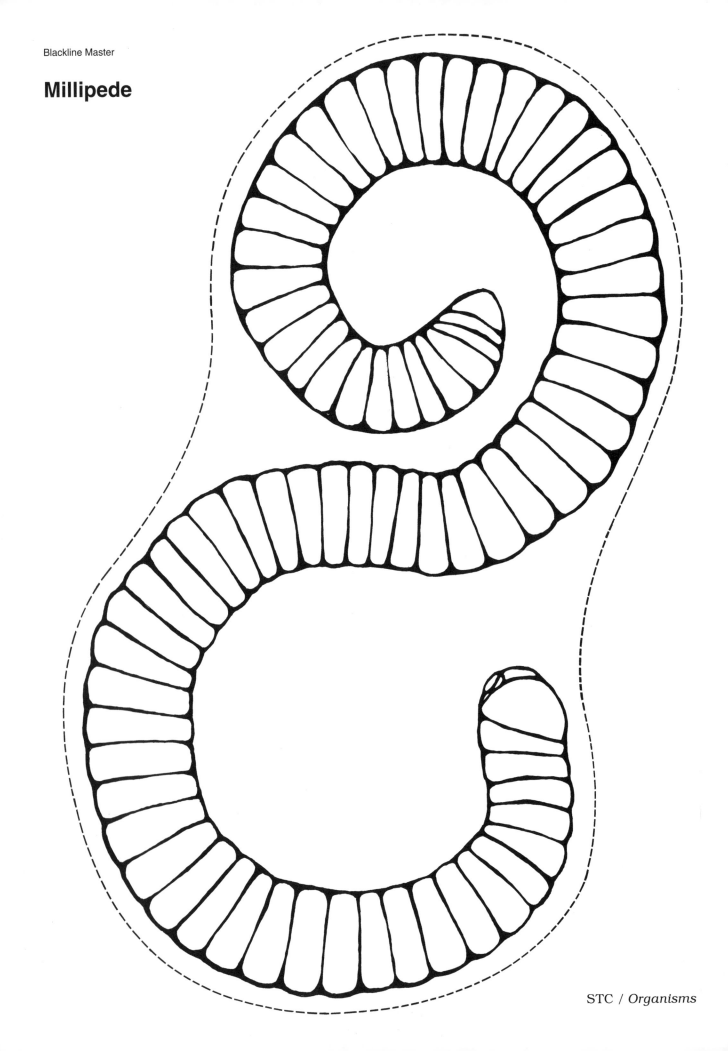

# Exploring Organisms Outside

By observing organisms outside the classroom, students may begin to apply their classroom experiences to all organisms, and to broaden their understanding that different kinds of organisms live in different kinds of places. Experiences in nature also may help motivate children to observe and explore the unknown.

When you choose an outdoor site, try to visit it before the activity day to make sure it fits the goals of the activity. Check for possible hazards. Be sure to allow enough time for travel to and from the site, work at the site, and a follow-up activity back in the classroom. Always tell the class the boundaries of each site and be sure students stay within them. Whenever possible, try to have another adult along.

1. Choose a park, meadow, or vacant lot with diverse plant and animal life. Before students enter the site, tell them to find as many different organisms as they can. You can use string to divide the area into "plots," one per student. Or you can have all students use the whole site. Have them write down or draw the organisms they find and where the organisms live. (Do not have them collect the organisms.) Encourage students to use descriptive words.

   Back in the classroom, list or describe all the organisms on the board and have students describe where they found them. Revisit the site after it rains. In what ways does the rain affect the diversity of organisms? Create a mural of the trip.

2. In out-of-the-way places on the schoolgrounds, have students build piles of grass clippings, leaves, and twigs about 15 cm (6 in) high. These piles should be in different areas such as woods, fields, or pavement. After a few days, ask students to collect the piles in plastic bags and spread them on white paper in the classroom. Have students look for organisms and observe and count how many kinds there are. Create a graph illustrating the diversity. Which pile contained the most organisms and/or the most diversity? Why?

   You can do a similar activity by placing a board on the ground in the woods, a meadow, or a field. After a week, look under the board with the class.

3. Have the class sit down on a lawn. Ask students to isolate as many different kinds of plants as they can, either by drawing or counting them. Create a graph. If you choose a fall day, also pick a place under a few trees where students can lie down, watch the leaves fall, and describe their observations. Then have the class collect, sort, and graph the leaves to illustrate the diversity of trees in your area.

4.  Choose a site with as much animal diversity as possible. Ask teams of two students to find an animal, such as an insect, worm, toad, or squirrel, to observe and follow for a few minutes. Have the teams record what the animal eats, where it goes, and whether it is alone or with other animals. Then ask teams to share their observations and demonstrate for the class how their animal moves.

5.  Go on a wildlife search on the school's grounds. Give students a few minutes to find an animal or a sign that one has been there, such as droppings, feathers, webs, or tracks. Bring students together to share what they have found. Then ask the class to list the animals that coexist on the grounds.

6.  Pick two environments in your area, such as a forest and a lake. Visit both sites and have students record the plants and animals they see in each. Back in the classroom, have students use drawings or magazine pictures to make a collection of organisms they have recorded. Then, using the pictures for each environment, create a tally graph. Which organisms were seen the most? Which were seen the least? Which organisms live in both places? Why can't all the organisms live in both places?

# National Science Resources Center Advisory Board

## Chair

Joseph A. Miller, Jr., Chief Technology Officer and Senior Vice President for Research and Development, DuPont Company, Wilmington, Del.

## Members

Ann Bay, Director, Office of Education, Smithsonian Institution, Washington, D.C.

DeAnna Banks Beane, Project Director, YouthALIVE, Association of Science-Technology Centers, Washington, D.C.

Fred P. Corson, Vice President and Director, Research and Development, The Dow Chemical Company, Midland, Mich.

Goéry Delacôte, Executive Director, The Exploratorium, San Francisco, Calif.

JoAnn E. DeMaria, Teacher, Hutchison Elementary School, Herndon, Va.

Peter Dow, Director of Education, Buffalo Museum of Science, Buffalo, N.Y.

Hubert M. Dyasi, Director, The Workshop Center, City College School of Education (The City University of New York), New York, N.Y.

Bernard S. Finn, Curator, Division of Information Technology and Society, National Museum of American History, Smithsonian Institution, Washington, D.C.

Robert M. Fitch, President, Fitch & Associates, Taos, N.M.

Jerry P. Gollub, John and Barbara Bush Professor in the Natural Sciences, Haverford College, Haverford, Pa.

Ana M. Guzmán, Vice President, Cypress Creek Campus and Institutional Campus Development, Austin Community College, Austin, Tex.

Anders Hedberg, Director, Center for Science Education, Bristol-Myers Squibb Pharmaceutical Research Institute, Princeton, N.J.

Richard Hinman, Senior Vice President (retired), Central Research Division, Pfizer Inc., Groton, Conn.

David Jenkins, Associate Director for Interpretive Programs, National Zoological Park, Smithsonian Institution, Washington, D.C.

Mildred E. Jones, Educational Consultant, Baldwin, N.Y.

John W. Layman, Director, Science Teaching Center, and Professor, Departments of Education and Physics, University of Maryland, College Park, Md.

Leon M. Lederman, Chair, Board of Trustees, Teachers Academy for Mathematics and Science, Chicago, Ill., and Director Emeritus, Fermi National Accelerator Laboratory, Batavia, Ill.

Sarah A. Lindsey, Science Coordinator, Midland Public Schools, Midland, Mich.

Lynn Margulis, Distinguished University Professor, Department of Botany, University of Massachusetts, Amherst, Mass.

Ted A. Maxwell, Associate Director, Collections and Research, National Air and Space Museum, Smithsonian Institution, Washington, D.C.

Mara Mayor, Director, The Smithsonian Associates, Smithsonian Institution, Washington, D.C.

John A. Moore, Professor Emeritus, Department of Biology, University of California, Riverside, Calif.

Carlo Parravano, Director, Merck Institute for Science Education, Rahway, N.J.

Robert W. Ridky, Program Director, Division of Undergraduate Education/Geosciences, National Science Foundation, Arlington, Va.

Ruth O. Selig, Executive Officer for Programs, Office of the Provost, Smithsonian Institution, Washington, D.C.

Maxine F. Singer, President, Carnegie Institution of Washington, Washington, D.C.

Robert D. Sullivan, Associate Director for Public Programs, National Museum of Natural History, Smithsonian Institution, Washington, D.C.

Gerald F. Wheeler, Executive Director, National Science Teachers Association, Arlington, Va.

Richard L. White, Executive Vice President, Bayer Corporation, Pittsburgh, Pa., and President of Fibers, Organics, and Rubber Division, and President and Chief Executive Officer, Bayer Rubber Inc., Canada

Paul H. Williams, Atwood Professor, Department of Plant Pathology, University of Wisconsin, Madison, Wis.

Karen L. Worth, Faculty, Wheelock College, and Senior Associate, Urban Elementary Science Project, Education Development Center, Newton, Mass.

## Ex Officio Members

Rodger Bybee, Executive Director, Center for Science, Mathematics, and Engineering Education, National Research Council, Washington, D.C.

E. William Colglazier, Executive Officer, National Academy of Sciences, Washington, D.C.

J. Dennis O'Connor, Provost, Smithsonian Institution, Washington, D.C.

Barbara Schneider, Executive Assistant for Programs, Office of the Provost, Smithsonian Institution, Washington, D.C.